PRAISE FOR UNLOCKING THE HEADACHE MYSTERY

"Elizabeth is a **superb companion and guide.** Join her on a **journey to freedom from headaches.**"

—David Buchholz, MD, Author, *Heal Your Headache: The 1-2-3 Program for Taking Charge of Your Pain*

"Anyone can read this book and realize their own ability to heal; how healing comes in many forms and guises but mostly from within. Ms. Phelps writes in beautiful prose filled with imagery and color. **A healing journey for everyone, not just headache sufferers and migraineurs.**"

—Elise Treff Gordon, MD, Family Medicine with Sports Medicine CAQ; United States Navy (retired)

"Elizabeth Phelps is not only a fine writer, she is a kind of headache whisperer with a gift for making these miseries disappear. Once a headache sufferer herself, she explored the subject through a combination of research, trial, error, study, and experience, and the result is this helpful and highly engaging book that almost anybody will find useful. **In these pages Elizabeth helps us tame the beast and keep it more permanently at bay.**"

—Frye Gaillard, Writer-in-Residence, University of South Alabama, award-winning author of *A Hard Rain*

"In *Unlocking the Headache Mystery* Elizabeth demonstrates, with passion and encyclopedic knowledge, how to prevent and deal with headaches in practical healing ways. **This is a well written, comprehensive guide, and an invaluable reference for the layperson, therapist and those interested in knowing more about headaches.**"

—Robert R. Maldonado, PhD, author of *The Calling of the Heart, A Journey in Self-Healing*

"Liz Phelps has compiled, with artistic flair, the key issues around headaches and their relief in a world being co-rocked by pandemic and a collapsed economy. Headaches are one of the most pervasive maladies being exacerbated at this time, and we can be grateful for this clear-spoken testament that breathes hope into our lives. **I urge the reader to get familiar with this book because you will see its chapters play out in your life every day.**"

—Brunie Emmanuel, Behavioral Health Consultant, The Uni-Vision Group

"*Unlocking the Headache Mystery* is a must-read for anyone who struggles with headaches or, for that matter, any health issue.** For those who are still relying heavily on traditional Western medicine, Elizabeth compassionately shows them the way out, illuminating science and telling her journey with authority and honesty. This book is a help to many—not just those suffering from headaches."

—Patrice Lively, Massage Therapist, Special Needs Pain Specialist

"**Here is a book to nourish the soul as it gives guidance to freeing oneself from debilitating headaches.** In *Unlocking the Headache Mystery* Elizabeth Phelps shares her journey, physically and spiritually, with wisdom and beauty of expression, introducing the reader to valuable practices, tips, and techniques that provide a solid place to begin healing."

—Carol Anne Brown, MSSW, Mental Health Counselor

"**If you are a headache sufferer, you need to read this thorough, intelligent book.** It is the culmination of research, a personal journey of courage and perseverance, and **a powerful gift to those who want to live a life free of headaches.** As stated in *Unlocking the Headache Mystery,* "Every creature arrives on Earth bearing elaborate gifts." The first time Elizabeth healed my headache with her hands and words, I knew she possessed a gift from God."

—Jennifer Glover, Communications Director

"**What a delightful way to learn, not just about headaches, but about life and the consequences of the many health choices we make.** Written in a way that everyone can relate to, it is a fun read. When Elizabeth drew the pulsing headache out of my body, I was left awestruck. It wasn't that I didn't believe it could happen, but that it actually *did* happen. There is no better way to learn than from one who has actually had the experience, and Elizabeth has had them all."

—Deborah Shook

Nothing is quite as compelling as following a good storyteller along her journey. Such is the case with *Unlocking the Headache Mystery* as the author shares knowledge obtained in her battle (and victory) to free herself from debilitating headaches. Spurred forward by a desire to learn causes and get her life back, Elizabeth explored, questioned, and experimented until she won. The result **is a plethora of techniques that offers the reader a road map to physical, mental, and spiritual well-being.**"

—Cheri Collins, Nuclear Energy Engineer and Speaker

"Certainly, *Unlocking the Headache Mystery* provides ways to stop and prevent headaches, but it also reflects ways to live life with a deeper understanding of our connection to the Earth and to one another. The writing is charming, clear, and always empathetic. Clearly, Elizabeth Phelps knows what life is like with headaches—and without them. **I am giving every friend who suffers with chronic headaches a copy of this book.**"

—Morgan Joseph Hamilton, PhD Candidate, Art Education

"As a previous major TMJ headache sufferer, I unequivocally find this book to contain answers to solving headache pain. From substantiated basics to uncommon, rarely discussed factors, it is an unusual but **trustworthy guide to personal growth and self-healing at the core level. *Unlocking the Headache Mystery* is a beautiful gift to anyone who reads it, even those who don't have headaches.**"

—Michael Wheeler, Creative Director, EarthGuest Arts & Music

"Elizabeth Phelps has masterfully detailed her journey through a maze of experiences associated with headaches and reveals to the reader a map of the many cause and effect links that could take a lifetime of suffering to uncover, comprehend, and put into perspective to assist one with an exit route from unnecessary suffering. **Loaded with detailed data and personal anecdotes, these pages will serve many in finding their way to freedom from debilitating headaches.** Her dedication to this noble cause of documenting these deep insights into what is to many a puzzling and seemingly inescapable conundrum is to be applauded."

—Vandorn Hinnant, Visionary Artist, and Author of *Paths to the Infinite*

UNLOCKING
THE
HEADACHE MYSTERY

Essential Keys to Reclaim
Your Vibrant Life

ELIZABETH ANSON PHELPS, CRP

Edited by Julia Stroud, Deborah Morgenthal, and Morgan Joseph Hamilton

Printed in the United States of America.

ISBN 978-1-7377308-0-4

Library of Congress Cataloging in Publication Data

Phelps, Elizabeth Anson (Phelps, Elizabeth Anne)

www.theheadachemystery.com

Unlocking the Headache Mystery, Essential Keys to
Reclaim Your Vibrant Life

1. Headaches   2. Migraines   3. Healing   4. Wellness   5. Mind and body

6. Holistic healing   7. Authenticity   8. Personal power

Manufactured in the United States of America

For Anson and Virginia Phelps, my parents,
heavenly doves, Annie & Anson,
and you, the reader—your vibrant life,
free of unnecessary pain,
amplifying beauty in this world and beyond.

If someone wishes for good health,
One must first ask oneself
if he is ready to do away with
the reasons for his illness.
Only then is it possible to help him.

Hippocrates

CONTENTS

PART II — SUBTLE MATTERS

PART III — EXTRAS

INTRODUCTION

Just off Highway 285, north of Santa Fe, a little adobe church sits quietly in the town of Chimayo. Every year, hundreds of thousands of pilgrims make their way to its holy ground. Some seek healing from the sacred red earth found in a small room to the side of the sanctuary. When I went for my bit of dirt in the fall of 1997, the walls of the room were lined with wheelchairs, crutches, and other items abandoned after miraculous healings.

As I stared at the assembled paraphernalia, I wondered, *How do you leave headaches on the wall?*

I asked my question at Chimayo during a desolate time. Migraine and muscle contraction headaches had ruled my life for twenty years. I felt hopeless because I thought the answer to my question was, "You can't. You can't leave headaches on the wall or anywhere else." At the time, I didn't know that Chimayo was just a pit stop on a longer journey that would allow me to gather the information in this book.

As I traveled the road to freedom from headaches, I met others who shared my affliction. That's when the journey presented me with a big surprise—an ability to release active headaches in fellow headache sufferers. One experience that convinced me that active headaches could be eliminated happened a few years after my visit to Chimayo.

I was washing my hands in a gas station restroom off the same New Mexico highway when a woman came in and commandeered the bathroom sink beside me. As we turned off our faucets and pulled brown paper towels from the wall rack, my hand-washing companion let out a little groan. That's when I took a good look at her. In the subatomic way humans analyze each other, the cause of her discomfort became obvious. As we finished drying our hands and tossed our soggy towelettes into the trash, I asked, "Do you have a headache?"

She pressed her fingers into her forehead and answered with a hissy "yesssss."

How well I knew the pain and desperation she was experiencing! The next thing I heard was my own voice, "I can help you with that."

We looked at each other, and after a tick-tock of silence, I added, "Want me to?"

Despite the odd nature of the offer, she agreed. (I have since found that headache folks always accept offers of relief—it's either a "Really?" or an up-and-down head nod, or a breathy "Pleeeease" or a "Yesssss." This is invariably a moment of excitement for me.

Ten minutes later, this particular headache victim stood before me, turning her head side to side. "It's gone!" she said, "It's really gone!"

I hovered on the edge of elation. "*Totally* gone?"

She nodded and said, with a huge smile, "Totally."

As I watched the relief and happiness transform her features, I did an inner dance of joy.

Then she asked, "Would you work on my husband? He's a dentist. He has an interview in Taos in an hour, and he has a headache."

I was momentarily stunned to find two people lined up for headache relief in a gas station, but answered, "Sure, if he wants me to. Do you want to ask him first?"

She left the bathroom to find her husband, who met me in front of the Cheetos rack. He was so tall his belt buckle was even with my chest, and I had to rise on tiptoe for much of our interaction. Although it was obvious that he wasn't entirely comfortable having a stranger "work on him" in a Chevron station, his headache abated.

Since the gas station experience, I have cared for hurting, headachy people in all sorts of places—hair salons, disaster-relief centers, living rooms, customer service desks, and churches. Each experience increased my desire to understand exactly how and why these interactions were effective.

On one occasion, I was working in the medical records department in a doctor's office when one of the nurses told me she had a headache. I gave her the "I can help you with that" line. She lobbed back a funny look but accepted the offer. Within ten minutes, her headache was gone.

A week later, the phone rang while the receptionist was at lunch, so I picked up the receiver and was met with a woman's voice begging from the other end of the line, "Can you get me an appointment *today?* I have a migraine. I can't live like this anymore."

Her words whooshed me back to a time when I had wept out those exact words to a friend: "I can't live like this anymore." So, I was especially quick to set up an emergency appointment. Then I headed down the hall in search of Dr. Flip Flop (so-called because she was cool enough to wear flip flops to work). I found her in her office.

"Hi, Dr. Flip Flop," I chirped.

She looked up from a chart. "Hey."

"How do you feel about woo-woo things?" I asked.

"What do you mean, '*woo-woo*' things?"

I explained my relationship to headaches and the general nature of my ability to "pull" headaches out of people. I used the word *woo-woo* to let her know I understood how bizarre my methods might sound, especially to a Western medical doctor. At best, they were hard to explain. At worst, unbelievable. After listening to my explanation, Dr. Flip Flop said, "When the patient arrives, we'll ask her if she wants to work with you. If she says yes, then go for it."

The patient arrived. She said yes. I went for it.

That is how I found myself sitting across from a woman who had suffered so much agony from headaches that she was willing to surrender herself to an unfamiliar healing process. Forty-five minutes later, she stood before me, smiling with relief. Headache gone.

After the session, Dr. Flip Flop met privately with the patient, then came to my desk beaming and said, "Thanks for curing my patient." That's when I heard the high-five celebratory news traveling up and down the hall. Dr. Flip Flop put her hand on my shoulder. "We'll tell all our neurology friends! The truth is, we doctors don't know *what* to do for headache patients. We can really use you." I felt such excitement!

My high lasted until Dr. Flip Flop's attorneys nixed the idea of my helping anybody—I was not a "legally insurable medical person." They were afraid patients would feel so good they'd leave the doctor's office, run a red light, then sue the doctor. But, despite the legal thumbs down, something beyond the status quo had been acknowledged. The fact that it was possible to quickly, non-invasively, eliminate an active headache held valuable implications for healing, and I was exuberant to have had the success confirmed by medical doctors.

Rapidly removing pain from someone's head is indeed meaningful and important, but it's not a permanent solution to vanquishing chronic head pain. Headaches are a puzzle requiring an understanding of mechanisms in the brain, contemplation, awareness, and peering at complicated puzzle pieces for extended periods of time. Each picture is individualized, so the pain-bearer is the only one who can complete it. Each piece of the puzzle must be arranged in proper proximity to the others, and each headache-holder is in charge of its placement. We cannot cram pieces into spaces where they do not fit, rather we must lay out the obvious cornerstone pieces, then use clues to try a piece here, another piece there, and keep going until the whole picture snaps into place.

I have no idea how many calculations take place when two creatures meet, but clearly, there are zillions of little notes being taken by mysterious forces in the field surrounding an individual; subtle messages are continuously transmitted through the mind and body—even the air around them. The only reason I knew the gas station lady had a headache was because my own headache hell had left me with the ability to recognize headaches in others. I could help Dr. Flip Flop's patient because of an amalgamation of abilities born from education, personal experience, training in alternative healing methods, intuition, hundreds of healing sessions, and thousands of headaches.

As a headache patient, I was privileged to learn from the giants of headache research: Diamond Headache Clinic, Cleveland Clinic, and other experts. Competitive sports and a degree in sports science provided knowledge about physiology, kinesiology, anatomy, and the power of mental focus. Master's studies in educational psychology honed my ability to understand the psycho-emotional dynamics of family systems, as did my work with at-risk youth and their families. Headaches drove me to therapists and to study Reiki, Polarity Therapy, Pranic Healing, yoga, and meditation. Looking back, it seems that every aspect of my life, from work to play, provided clues on the path that led to healing. After I understood my headaches, I was able to help others solve their headache dilemmas.

According to the World Health Organization (*How Common Are Headaches?* February 11, 2014), "Up to one adult in twenty has a headache every–or nearly every—day," with at least "one adult in every seven in the world" being affected by migraine-type headaches. They also identify headache as the third leading cause of disability worldwide.

There is a tremendous body of knowledge pertaining to "types" of headaches. The International Headache Society classifies 150 types, and organizations dedicated to treating these chronic miseries often classify headache disorders as either "primary" or "secondary" headaches.

Primary headaches include tension, migraine, and cluster headaches, and are *not* the result of another medical condition. Secondary headaches include medication overuse and sinus headaches. My formal diagnosis was migraine with muscle-contraction headaches. Despite classifications, all I knew was that my head hurt and I wanted it to stop.

For the migraine-ridden: my use of the term "headaches" includes migraines, but every topic in this book bears the potential to ease and play a role in eliminating all forms of *chronic* headaches. It excludes 911-type sudden-onset headaches.

In *Unlocking the Headache Mystery*, I share, chapter by chapter, what I discovered during my search for answers and relief. I wrote it as a simple guide that includes methods, research, and personal stories. Some topics, like hydration, are straightforward, but others require diving into the shadowy corners of one's beliefs. Rest assured, you do not have to take that dive unless you want to. Think of this book as a *discussion* about the potential benefits of adjusting habits and perceptions. You alone will determine if and when you are ready to address each topic.

My path to freedom from headaches began with neurologists, CAT scans, MRIs, biofeedback sessions, and prescription drugs. Injections, allergy tests, junkets to the ER, and hospital stays soon followed. There were days when I, and everyone around me, could scarcely bear the suffering. It's impossible to count the days and nights I spent in darkened rooms, smashing my fingers into my head, wearing ice bags like they were hats. I was desperate to find solutions not typically forthcoming from the world of Western medicine.

My search eventually took me on a journey across the country, alone. My only form of communication was a borrowed portable CB radio. I participated in Lakota sweat lodges and stayed in monasteries. I tested myself by climbing thirty-foot mountain faces. Because I traveled alone, I could hear my inner voice instead of the voices of other people or cultural demands. I hiked and drove and listened to the directions emitted from within. I learned how miracles behave. Clues appeared along my trail like bread crumbs, leading me to experiences that revealed the crucial communication systems that connect humans and forces beyond everyday awareness. I read. I studied. I experimented.

I had two escorts on my excursion: Pain, who demanded the journey, and Belief, who whispered encouragement as I sniffed out answers on the paths I traveled. There were so many paths my nose got tired. Although Belief's knees often wobbled beneath me, they always held me up.

My journey through headaches taught me about the intricate and marvelous nature of human beings and our relationship to the body, spirit, mind, and healing. I learned that the pain that expresses itself beneath a skull where fingers cannot reach, actually *can* be reached—there are a variety of ways to access it. Headaches are caused, and solutions are always inherent within causes.

This book is a collection of practices and experiences that helped me eliminate headaches. I hope it offers new perspectives to you, the sufferer. My return to health required thirty-five years of searching; it was the only way I could find answers because there was no book—no resource— that discussed, or linked the multitude of factors that affect headaches. That's why I have packed this volume with everything I've learned—so you don't have to travel the same long road.

HOW TO USE THIS BOOK

Each chapter of this book focuses on a specific topic, suggests solutions, and includes personal stories that offer insight into your headache dilemma. Each topic ties directly into a platform where healing headaches begins—a migraine mechanism that exists in every human brain. This mechanism involves a threshold and how many triggers it can bear. Some thresholds are spacious, others cramped. As you read this book and make new daily decisions, it's crucial to remember that this migraine mechanism is always at play. You may be surprised at what can trigger a headache. (Who suspects an avocado?)

The best explanation of the operations of this all-important mechanism is found in the book, *Heal Your Headache: The 1-2-3 Program for Taking Charge of Your Pain*, by David Buchholz, MD, Neurology Specialist, Johns Hopkins

Medicine. Please read it. The bottom line is that anyone with headaches must minimize their trigger load and increase their threshold (tolerance). Examples of how to do this run rampant throughout this volume, but your success ultimately depends on you managing your threshold to trigger ratio because a threshold overtaken by triggers results in a headache. And, of course, the last thing you want to do is reduce your threshold with pain killers that cause rebound headaches and leave no way out, or eat foods that invite headaches. While all of the chapters in *Unlocking the Headache Mystery* are important, the issues of food and medicine really need to be addressed early because as long as they are creating headache havoc, they will be pouring gasoline on a fire you are trying to put out.

You may have been searching for one solution—one magic bullet fix. A pill. A procedure. One problem with one answer. In my case, and quite possibly yours, many components were at play. That's why the fastest way to disassemble headaches is to address multiple factors simultaneously. Two, three, or all of the topics in these pages may relate to your headaches, but only you will know which subjects apply. (The Food and Medicines & Doctors chapters apply to everyone.)

Just think of each chapter as a piece of a larger puzzle. Take your time. If you need a rest period from applying these methods, or even reading about them, just put the book down and come back to it when you feel like it. And for goodness sake, listen to your body—it knows everything. If you pay attention to what it's saying, you will naturally evolve away from headaches.

For emphasis, some concepts are repeated throughout the book. Just relax as you read and be open to any stirrings that inspire you to consider new possibilities for healing. As always, it's vital to rule out medical issues before you take on new practices, including those in this book.

One more thing. Please don't get nervous when I use the word "God," or synonyms for God, like "The Creator" and "The Great Mystery." It's my way of elevating the mysterious, rich nature of the forces that exist beyond concrete human perception—a way to keep them from falling into automatic, compartmentalized definitions. When I use "God," think of your own larger meaning and use *your* definition. When I reach for *my* meaning, I see my life as a fantastic gift. I consider everything I am, everything I have learned, and even the lessons of headaches as gifts.

This book is my gift to you.

Now let's focus on remedies to ease your mind and body. I recommend reading the chapters in order from beginning to end. Chapters 1-28 discuss straightforward remedies. They provide verifiable information at the beginning of each chapter, followed by examples of my personal experience with the topic. You probably already know some of the basics, but please read them anyway because they form a foundation for more complicated matters discussed in later chapters. Chapters 29-43 combine complex, intangible concepts with personal stories and research that illustrate viewpoints you may find worthy of your consideration. Items on the *Suggested Readings and Videos* list provide expanded, interesting, and important health-related perspectives from well-known experts. Blank pages for taking notes are available at the back of the book.

As you turn these pages, I travel with you.

Elizabeth

THE
BASICS

ICE

Whatever beauty we behold,
the more it is distant, serene, and cold,
the purer and more durable it is.
It is better to warm ourselves with ice than with fire.

Henry David Thoreau

Our journey begins with one of the simplest, most immediate aids to anyone with a headache—ice. Ice is invaluable because it quickly constricts blood vessels, reduces inflammation, and provides a respite from pain, providing much-needed rest. Ice gives us a toehold on our way to a headache-free life.

Fortunately, there are numerous ways to apply ice to one's head: old-fashioned ice bags, gel packs—even ice-pack hats. Medium-sized gel packs are an excellent choice because they are tidy and cover an appropriate surface area. Some of them last up to eight hours (handy when traveling), and come with a thin, soft pouch and a Velcro strap so you can attach the compress to your head (or a sore lower back). The icy cold brings speedy relief, and the pouch and strap allow you to apply the appropriate amount of pressure, which can also reduce head pain.

Get at least two cold packs so you always have an extra in the freezer, ready for use. An eight-hour cold pack is an excellent choice, although you'll want to intermittently remove the pack from your head so blood can flow back into the affected area. Most physicians recommend twenty minutes on and twenty minutes off, but I used to sleep with packs all night. Do your own research, and listen to your body for advice.

Ice brings such instantaneous relief that the need for medicine is often reduced or eliminated. Once you have alleviated the pain, you can investigate the root causes of the headaches and introduce alternative methods of resolving them.

Try ice.

Experiences with Ice

I lived with incapacitating headaches for fifteen years before discovering ice. As an inpatient at the Diamond Headache Clinic in Chicago, my doctor's first instruction was to jettison the pain medicine I had been taking for seven years. I felt scared and vulnerable, and wondered, *What happens if I get a headache?* An answer soon arrived.

One day when I was in a wrestling match with an Olympian-style headache, a nurse came to my room to check on me. The headache was so bad she gave me an injection. As the nurse was leaving, she turned back from the door and asked, "Would you like some ice?"

I peeked at her from under my bedcovers. "Ice?"

She stared at me. "You don't know about *ice*?"

No. I did not know about ice, but once I did, ice and I became best friends. I reveled in it. Ice, ice, ice. Old-fashioned ice bags were incredibly effective because they got very cold, but they also leaked on my pillows and hair, so gel packs became invaluable.

Major headaches required four gel packs: one behind, one over the top, and one on each side of my head. Velcro straps made it easy to shift the contraption around. I slept with it like a refrigerated dance partner and wore it like a hat when I had to function during the day.

I lived like that for years.

HEAT

Always keep your body filled with light and heat.

Morihei Ueshiba

In opposition to the constrictive nature of ice, heat expands and calms the body. *Moist* heat, in particular, brings welcome relief to the tight neck and shoulder muscles that often accompany headaches.

Applying moist heat can be as simple as wetting a towel with hot water, wringing it out, and draping it around the back of the neck and shoulders. When the towel cools, reheat it, and continue applying it until the muscles release. Deep-breathing aids the process. The temperature of the water should be hot but safe. Moist-heat heating pads are also available, some of which contain beads or seeds that are microwaveable—a mess-free way to relax musculature using heat.

Hot stone therapy is another effective way to soothe and release muscle tissue. This method replaces heated towels and heating pads with hot, smooth basalt rocks. During a massage, a therapist strategically places the stones so their heat can penetrate and relax muscles. The combination of deep heat and massage therapy makes it hard for a headache to survive. Be sure to request hot stone therapy when you make your massage appointment because the stones have to be pre-heated.

Hot showers and warm baths (not hot) are also allies in the effort to decompress the body and bring a sense of comfort that ameliorates stress-related conditions—especially headaches. A good, warm-water shampoo relaxes tight scalp muscles while reducing overall tension. More about warm-water treatments in the *Healing Waters* chapter.

Experiences with Heat

Hot moist towels often brought relief to the tight neck and shoulder muscles that accompanied my headaches. To get the towel hot, I dunked it (with the burner off) in a simmering pot of water. After wringing out the towel, I draped it around my neck and shoulders, then re-dunked to keep the towel hot, repeating the process until my muscles released. When my muscles relaxed, so did the headache.

My physical constitution tends to be tight, so massage therapists use moist, heated towels to relax my musculature before massaging a specific muscle group. The heat "talks" to the muscle, sending soothing warmth into tissues before the deeper bodywork begins. Hot stone therapy possesses an almost magical ability to release my muscle tension. More than once, I have left a hot stone massage and wept out of gratitude for the relief it provided.

Letting hot water splash on my neck and shoulders in the shower, or just putting my feet in warm water, helps pull the plug on the generalized tension that can build up in my body. A bathtub filled with warm water is my in-home version of a natural hot spring, bringing welcome relief from pent-up stress. I use baths to both prevent and assuage headaches.

3

WATER

Water is the driving force of all nature.

Leonardo da Vinci

Water consumption is especially vital for headachy people. Water keeps things flowing, lubricates, eliminates, keeps the sludge-level down, and frees the body to operate at top level; drinking water is like keeping clean oil in the family car. Water helps keep fascia (the thin casing of connective tissue that surrounds muscle and organs) from sticking, and is vital for eliminating knots and tension in the body, including the areas directly related to headaches: shoulders, neck, jaws, and scalp.

Water loss is a natural process, so we need to constantly replenish our supply because even mild dehydration can impact the body, brain function, and mood. Seasonal heat and physical exertion increase the need for sufficient hydration.

Prescription medicines can also rob the body of water, as evidenced by the constipation they can bring (another problem for headache sufferers). Top off dehydration with a low-pressure system and a full moon (the moon controls the tides inside your body as well as the oceans), and you've got yourself a real headache hoedown. Some people may drink *too* much water, but that would be a matter for one's own deep awareness, and perhaps, a discussion with your physician. Commonly recommended water intake is from ten to thirteen cups a day, depending on a variety of factors like body weight and climate. To reap the full benefits of water you'll want to drink it regularly throughout the day, because if you wait until you're thirsty, you have waited too long.

If you drink coffee (more about coffee in the *Food* chapter), remember to drink enough water to compensate for any diuretic effects of caffeine. Also, be sure the water is filtered, and avoid drinking from plastic bottles because they leach estrogen into the water.

Think *pure* water.

Drink good, clean water.

Experiences with Water

Most of my life has been spent as a competitive athlete with a go-getter personality. In my twenties, for five days a week, I worked eight hours a day followed by three hours of competitive sports training. Later in my life, I continued to attack athletic endeavors with the fervor of a young Bruce Lee (I was deep into karate). Water was the last thing on my mind.

Every night after working out, I ate dinner, then went to bed dehydrated. During the night my muscles and tendons shortened and knotted up until I felt like monster hands were gripping my hamstrings, shoulders, neck, and scalp. The connective tissue between my joints also contracted. Unbeknownst to me, those locked muscles and tight joints helped set the stage for relentless headaches. At the time, I did not understand the value of water.

When I drink sufficient water, my muscles operate smoothly, and I am better able to avoid headaches. Hydration is even more effective when I combine it with other healthy choices like eating natural foods, getting plenty of deep sleep, and stretching after exercising. When I want to drink something more exotic than water, I drink pure pomegranate juice which not only tastes great but supplies a dose of potassium that helps maintain my muscle health.

My body knows when I'm taking care of it, so when it talks, I listen.

#4

SLEEP

Sleep that knits up the ravell'd sleave of care,
The death of each day's life, sore labour's bath,
Balm of hurt minds, great nature's second course,
Chief nourisher in life's feast.

Shakespeare, *Macbeth*

Your body knows how to repair itself during sleep. This 'night crew' makes little repairs to our physical and mental systems by removing toxins from the cerebrospinal fluid that surrounds the brain and spinal cord. The cleansing process requires between seven to eight hours of quality sleep.

Sleep keeps us sharp; it improves concentration, reasoning, memory, clarity, and learning. It is required for critical thinking, alertness, and starting the day in a good mood. Sleep is a best friend that wards off everything from depression and forgetfulness to low libido and inflammation. It keeps our skin healthy, bones strong, and assists in maintaining muscle mass.

Sleep is a priceless commodity, and it behooves us to understand it because even short-term sleep deprivation can muck-up our minds and bodies and cause headaches. (*Long-term* sleeplessness is connected to diseases like type 2 diabetes, heart ailments, and obesity.)

The body runs on an internal clock that manages a cycle of physiological processes that operate in the brain. This clock is called the circadian rhythm, and it uses temperature and light to tell us when to sleep, rise, and eat. At night it increases the output of the hormone melatonin, which makes us sleepy.

There are five stages of sleep. These stages occur in cycles and play an important role in ensuring restorative sleep and health. It takes about ninety minutes to cycle through all five stages. If you have ever taken a nap and awakened refreshed, you probably completed the entire ninety-minute cycle.

The fifth stage of sleep is the well-known, all-important REM (rapid eye movement) sleep. REM sleep is the la-la land where dreaming occurs. Its distinctive characteristic is rapid eye movement. The brain in REM mode becomes very active, maybe *more* active than when we are awake. The eye movements are suspected to occur as the brain observes the mental images in our dreams. Researchers at London's Institute of Cognitive Neuroscience believe REM is crucial for consolidating and encoding memory, especially the kind that helps us learn new information and solve problems. REM also maintains neural pathways.

Scientists do not know why dream activity is crucial for healthy brains, but they agree that adequate REM sleep is vital. When sleep is interrupted, REM is often the stage that is sacrificed. During a full night of *quality* sleep, however, our brains have an opportunity to do the deep cleaning that removes neurotoxins, such as waste products from a substance called *beta-amyloid* which is found in the brains of people with Alzheimer's.

Food, habits, and emotional issues can affect our sleep patterns. Complex carbs, like pasta, improve sleep because they increase levels of tryptophan. Tryptophan, magnesium, calcium, and vitamin B6 help produce melatonin which is responsible for regulating circadian rhythms. Some foods enhance serotonin production or possess vitamins and minerals conducive to sleep. Choose kiwi, tart cherry juice, fish, fiber (chia seeds, whole grains, nuts), dark leafy greens, walnuts, dates, and calcium-fortified natural yogurt. Stay away from sugar and caffeine.

For your evening meal, you might include foods that remind you of happy childhood days. How about mashed potatoes? Rice with butter? Ensure that you drink enough water to keep your body hydrated until morning, but not so much you have to make a beeline for the bathroom all night.

If something is bothering you emotionally, resolve the issue immediately. Make the call or write the letter; you don't have to mail it. Cry, paint, beat drums. When I find myself troubled by something minor, I try to take action before I crawl between the sheets. If I wonder, *Did I leave the garage door open?* I immediately get up and check it.

Good habits also encourage sleep. I am not a perfect housekeeper, but I sleep better when my house is in order. Subconsciously I know I'll wake up to a neat, clean home.

Consider, too, your bedroom décor. Create a beautiful, peace-filled atmosphere that supports relaxation. Decorate it with softness: twilight blue or soft green walls. Keep it simple. Use soft fabrics. Include a vase of flowers. If you like essential oils, mix a drop or two of a peace-producing oil in a spray bottle of distilled water and lightly spritz the room fifteen minutes before bedtime. Buy a luscious set of sheets. If you have a slim budget, make this a priority anyway because comfortable sheets support your health. Amplify their effect by taking a warm bath before you go to bed. Remember to darken your sleeping room and cover illuminated clocks or replace them with a charming old-fashioned wind-up clock. In situations when you cannot darken the room, use a sleep mask.

Sleep comes more easily after a pleasant evening. Horror movies, disturbing images, and the news are predominantly worrisome. Fortunately, you can control your exposure by turning off the television. The same choice applies to books, the internet, conversations, and negative people. Everything we see and hear affects us. It's a good idea to simply stop working, unplug, and enjoy quietude in the evening. There is a reason thatched bungalows on the shore and remote cabins on wooded hillsides are restful.

Before bedtime, give yourself at least two hours away from those mind-altering blue lights inherent in computer and tech screens (blue light affects melatonin). Many people drape a piece of fabric over their computers and other screens when they are not using them; blocking the screens essentially hides them, which encourages people to be present with one another.

Also recommended: remove televisions and cell phones from your bedroom.

Instead of using technology, let the spirit of the night lead you to peaceful endeavors. Learn to play the ukulele or cards or ping pong—whatever is delightful and calming to you. Sit outside and listen to the birds nestling into the bushes before nightfall. Notice how energetic bird calls soften, then lessen, before all is quiet. Copy the birds.

Once you are in bed, set the intention to sleep soundly. Tell yourself you are going to trust, let go, and sleep. Talking to the benevolent, mysterious force I call God has a profound effect on my ability to sleep. There is something restful in connecting with wisdom greater than mine, and with so much evidence under my belt, it is easy for me to put myself into the capable hands of the Great Mystery, the Great Big All. I pray anyway I choose: mad, scared, grateful. Did you see Tom Hanks in the movie, *Joe and the Volcano*? He lies half-dead on a raft in the ocean when the bright light of an epic full moon rises above the horizon and awakens him. He staggers to standing position, then, with reverent awe, says, "Thank you for my life." The depth and authenticity of his gratitude are inspirational. Try to find and express your raw gratitude. It works wonders. Say thank you to yourself, too; kiss the back of your hands goodnight.

Before you know it . . . ZZzzzzzzzzzzz

The topic of sleep requires a discussion about mattresses and pillows because they are the foundation on which we slumber. Mattresses are made in many ways, ranging from coiled spring to waterbed, latex to memory foam. They are made to meet your personal preferences, ranging from soft to firm, hot to cold. Because your choice of mattress is crucial to resolving your headaches, take time to research and experiment before you make your purchase. One way to mattress-test is to spend the night with various friends; think of Goldilocks and the three bears, and pick the mattress that is "just right." You can also test bedding by staying at hotels that provide quality mattresses.

For headache relief, bedding should remain cool throughout the night. Memory foam mattresses used to be notorious for holding heat, although new models have incorporated cooling technologies. Cooling mattress pads are also available.

The ultimate goal of a pillow is to place the head and neck in comfortable alignment. Of course, a pillow that keeps the head cool helps defeat headaches. Pillow types range from latex and foam to seed pillows. Buckwheat hull pillows keep the head reasonably cool and can be manipulated to conform to the shape of one's head and neck. Some seed pillows include a zipper which makes it easy to customize the density of the pillow. Small pieces of foam can be mixed with the seed hulls, allowing further modification of the pillow's texture. If you choose a buckwheat hull pillow, be sure the hulls are purified. The Regenisis pillow by Pur-Sleep™ is an excellent, adjustable buckwheat hull pillow. There are other cooling pillows on the market, and the only way to find your perfect fit is to search for it.

Experiences with Sleep

My mind is a cracker-jack thinker in the morning— when I get a good night's sleep. If I'm writing, searching for a synonym for "cranky person," the word *curmudgeon* will effortlessly appear. If I did *not* get enough sleep, my mind function is so poor I may as well skip work and play tiddlywinks. Before my headaches abated, they frequently ruined my sleep, wreaked mayhem on my circadian rhythms, and robbed me of innumerable productive, joyful days.

During my mother's declining years, I became so stressed and tired I couldn't string two thoughts together. I wondered if I was getting dementia. It turned out to be a combination of emotional overload and a lack of quality sleep.

Anytime I am sleep-deprived, I run the risk of inviting a headache into my life. Even after I had essentially terminated my headaches, I ran into trouble when my cat, Balthezar, went through a phase of yowling intermittently throughout the night. My sleep was so disturbed I experienced a recurrence of headaches. The solution was to settle Balthezar in another room. After I solved the problem, my sanity returned and the headaches stopped.

I didn't know how much a bed could affect my health until I bought a quality mattress. Not only did the right mattress allow me to get a good night's sleep, it resolved the low back discomfort that, unbeknownst to me, had been exacerbating the headaches. I had previously tried standard coil mattresses, pillow-tops, waterbeds, and latex. Even when I purchased the supportive bed, it took me two tries to get it right. The first mattress I bought felt good when I lay on it in the store, but my back went catawampus when I slept on it at home. I traded it for a firm mattress that aligned my body correctly and worked magic on eliminating my headaches.

My search for a comfortable pillow involved a lot of trial and error. I tried solid latex, latex chunks, curvy, fluffy, and foam pillows. None of them supported my head and neck comfortably. My pillow quandary was finally solved by a buckwheat hull pillow that allowed me to adjust the quantity of seeds via a zipper in the pillow's construction. I had to get accustomed to the rustle of the hulls as they swished inside the casing, but I eventually stopped noticing the sound. My buckwheat hull pillow is smaller than standard, which makes it very portable.

#5

LIGHT

I will love the light for it shows me the way,
yet I will endure the darkness for it shows me the stars.

Og Mandino

Almost anyone who has had a headache can attest to the additional pain caused by bright light. Photosensitivity is common to headache folks, which should be no surprise since headache-prone people are usually sensitive in every other way—we are the proverbial canaries in the coalmine of humanity, catching every nuance of our environments.

Researchers have now proven that red light and blue light (computer screens, televisions, cell phones) have a particularly nasty effect on people, exacerbating head pain because red and blue rays generate the largest number of signals in the cortex and retina—good for ramping up cognitive function, but lousy at inducing a sense of calm. Headache-prone people need calm. Green light generates the smallest number of signals and can reduce pain. Even though

18

there are currently no sources for affordable green-tinted sunglasses or light bulbs, there are some things one can do to reduce photosensitivity. When eating at a restaurant, sit facing away from light sources. In an office, sit near a window, away from flickering lights. Avoid fluorescent lights; opt for soft-light lamps. Keep a good pair of amber-tinted sunglasses on hand. Purchase a good, comfortable eye mask, and bedeck your windows with blackout window shades or curtains; the additional darkness will ensure a good night's sleep which also reduces sensitivity.

Experiences with Light

One of the worst phases of my life with headaches occurred in my twenties. Without knowing it, I was participating in behaviors that made the headaches worse: over-exercising, over-working, getting little sleep, and eating junk food. I was one whizz-bang dynamo of self-destruction. In the midst of a particularly brutal and long-winded headache, the light coming from my bedroom windows was exacerbating the pain. My parents closed the drapes in an attempt to blackout the room but also had to cover the windows with thick blankets because even the *slightest* light amplified my pain. It was three special days of hell for everyone.

Also, during my headache years, I spent extensive hours working in a stressful job in an office with fluorescent lighting. The only thing that saved me was turning out the lights and wearing sunglasses. I worked like a mole. Fortunately, I owned brown-based sunglasses that soothed my aching eyes. A desk lamp provided soft, peace-evoking light that improved the working atmosphere and further reduced the negative effects of light on my sensitive eyes and overall disposition.

In experiencing the effects of light, I learned the value of pitch black darkness. I found extraordinary relief in a totally blacked-out room because absolute darkness had the effect of silencing overworked aspects of my taxed mind and body. The absence of light allowed me to truly turn off—like a shutdown overheated, overworked computer. In the quiet space that remained, I was able to release tension and headaches.

As I modified my life and learned more about myself, the headaches began to diminish until finally, bright light no longer had a deleterious effect on my eyes or triggered headaches.

#6

HEALING WATERS

In one drop of water are found all the secrets of all the oceans;
in one aspect of You are found all the aspects of existence.

Kahlil Gibran Jr.

Certain bodies of water are known for their healing qualities: hot springs, mountain pools, waterfalls, creeks, streams, lakes, and oceans. You are fortunate if you live near one.

Ojo Caliente outside Santa Fe boasts natural warm-water springs and an array of healing waters—even arsenic water. The springs by the Rio Grande in Taos, New Mexico, provide both freshwater adventure *and* serenity—perfect for dismantling headaches. Crashing ocean waves and waterfalls bathe us in oxygen-amplifying, mood-elevating negative ions.

One of my favorite healing waters is the Gulf of Mexico, but almost any salty sea promotes healing. Salt water purifies, and because it is buoyant, it's the perfect medium for floating, relaxing, and detoxifying the body. Salt detoxifies through the pores on our skin.

Of course, it's wise to check the health of any water source before wading in, because some bodies of water contain unfriendly bacteria—an important consideration for anyone with open cuts or scrapes.

On the occasions you cannot get to a salty ocean or other healing water, a warm bath can serve as a miniature ocean by simply adding salt to the water—any kind of salt, although Dead Sea salt is my favorite. Some companies specialize in sea salt and provide an affordable way to buy in bulk. A variety of salt crystal sizes is available. A blend of fine and medium-grained salts is useful for both salt scrubs and baths. Epsom salt is very effective—four cups in a bath induces a noticeable, sweet sedation to the system. Use care when getting into a saltwater tub—they can be slippery: allow the salt to dissolve, and hold on to something stable as you step in. A few drops of a fragrant essential oil provides additional soothing effects.

Another way to invite relaxation is to wet a handful of salt with warm water, lace it with almond oil (or another oil), and gently scrub your hands and forearms. When you rinse, use temperate water and envision all tension going down the drain. A salt scrub can also be used on the feet and lower legs, resulting in immediate stress relief.

Hot tubs are enticing because they symbolize relaxation, but headache-prone people should approach them with caution—they can wreak havoc on the vascular system. You can avoid launching hot water headaches by paying attention to your specific physiology. (Mine prohibits the use of hot tubs.)

Some spas place cold water plunge tubs near their hot tubs. Clients heat up in the tubs, then jump into a vat of icy water—most invigorating! Aside from the physiological effects of vascular constriction, the sheer shock snaps the mind into a zippy state of attention. Those individuals with heart and vascular issues will want to consider any health issues before engaging in cold water plunges. Consult your good sense, and ask for advice when you are unsure.

Do some experiments with water—even soaking one's feet in heated water can pull blood and its accompanying pressure away from the head. In severe situations, you might strap ice packs to the skull and drape heated moist towels on the neck and shoulders while immersing the feet in warm water. Try various combinations, remembering to focus on deep relaxation. Let water rinse all headache-causing tension from your mind and body.

Experiences with Healing Waters

A beach environment always settles my mind and body. Ocean waves fill my system with negative ions, oxygen, and serenity. When it's warm enough to swim, the salt water supplies numerous benefits: the comfort of water, a reminder of the safe sensation an embryo feels when floating in its mother's womb, and the squeaky-clean feeling delivered through salt, sun, sand, and bare feet. Salt water is so healing that whenever I have a cut, a swim in the ocean speeds its disappearance. I also welcome the baptismal quality of water and let it purify any clinging dregs of mental and emotional negativity. As I emerge from the sea, I consciously allow the dross of life to fall away. When the beach is not an option, a bath of warm water with sea or Epsom salt provides an alternate way to bring me into a relaxed condition.

Another tribute to saltwater healing goes to the warm waters of Key West, Florida. An overzealous run to first base resulted in a torn quadricep that put me on crutches during a vacation with my family. The injury left me watching from the shore while everyone else snorkeled and swam around laughing. The eighth day, tired of being left out, I hijacked a pair of diving fins and joined in the fun—even though I could barely paddle my legs. The next day I was able to walk without the crutches. Weightless, gentle movement and saltwater were great physical therapists.

My physical nature cannot tolerate hot water baths, and I have learned that to enter a hot tub is to invite a beast of a headache to join me. I once followed the instructions for a detox bath using fresh walnut extract: "Make the water as hot as you can tolerate." The hot, hot water made a pre-existing headache *much* worse. After that experience, I stuck with temperate salt baths.

I learned the benefits of cold water therapy when I was nine. My best friend, Mary, and I devised a bathtime contest. The winner was determined by how many seconds she could endure the coldest water showering down full-blast: "1, 2, 3, 4, 5 . . ." When the contestant neared the point of shivering, she'd signal by saying, "Okay, okay," and the water would be switched to hot: "1, 2, 3, 4 . . ." Mary and I sometimes played this hot-cold game for half an hour. It was great fun, and I now wonder if we weren't little health sages because of the following story.

On a trip to Vancouver, Canada, I had my usual, distracting headache when friends suggested a hike to a mountain pool. My friend, Luke, pointed to the water and said, "I'll tell you how to cure a headache—jump in!" I cocked my head, stared at him, then jumped in. After a maximum of two seconds underwater, I shot to the surface gasping for air, thinking I was dying—the icy water seemed to have shut down my vascular system. After I *levitated* back to the shore, the blood rushed back into my veins, and I felt most alive. Very tingly, indeed. The headache had almost disappeared.

My eldest brother, Anson, did not typically have headaches, but a big one rolled over him during his finals at art school. He had gone days without sleep and was running on fumes. Anson said his head hurt so badly he plunged it into a sink filled with ice cubes and cold water. *Voilá!* He came out wet but much improved. I never tried his method.

7

ESSENTIAL OILS

Nature itself is the best physician.

Hippocrates

Plants have been used for healing since ancient times and their essences and essential oils are among nature's purest medicines. Each oil carries signature properties that support healthy mental, emotional, and physical states that help unravel headaches.

Essential oils can be used in a variety of ways. Some oils are effective when diffused into the air, while others are more beneficial when applied directly to the skin. Oils in bathwater (a few drops of lavender) induce a state of calmness. Ingested, a few drops of wild orange can turn a glass of water into a healthy, flavorful drink. A cotton ball infused with essential oil (rosemary, frankincense, clove) creates a pleasant work environment. A combination of lavender and peppermint oil is effective in releasing muscle tension. Straight peppermint oil tingles on the skin and operates as a smokescreen that relieves pain, and is very effective when applied to the back of the neck, shoulders, jaws, forehead, and temples.

Some oils carry archetypical elements that are encoded in their fragrances. Rose oil, for instance, evokes a sense of beauty and wealth. Frankincense, of Biblical fame, brings a sense of the sacred to one's day.

Lemon oil is good for cooking and making lemonade, but because lemons are on the food list of possible headache triggers, lemon oil may require a bit of experimentation. A drop of eucalyptus oil is particularly nice in a bath because it improves breathing and oxygen intake, both of which are calming. A blend of orange, tangerine, ylang-ylang, and blue tansy also creates a relaxing effect.

One way to apply essential oils is to place a few drops on the inside of the left wrist, then place the right wrist over the drops, and circle the top wrist clockwise three times. The rhythm of three wrist rotations connects you with the mind, body, and spirit, or air, earth, sea, or the Trinity. (Use *your* connection points.) After circling the wrists, raise both wrists to the nose and take three, slow, deep breaths and mentally release all tension in your mind and body. Set an intention to let go. With practice, this ritual develops the calmness so crucial to headache release.

There are hundreds of oils with differing characteristics, so it's important to obtain a reference guide that includes detailed information about each oil. Be sure the guide contains a section that discusses contraindications for specific conditions such as pregnancy or high blood pressure. One of my favorite reference books is *Reference Guide for Essential Oils* by Connie and Alan Higley because it contains simple, yet thorough, information. Classes about essential oils are available through healers like massage therapists and reflexologists who provide participants with the opportunity to ask questions and sample each oil.

While essential oils are natural medicines, it's important to understand them. Yes, they are concentrated elixirs made by the Creator of the Universe, but the Creator made hemlock, too, and you don't want to drink it. And some oils are "hot" (like peppermint oil); they possess a burning effect, and must be kept away from eyes, pets, and children. Always test hot oils on a small area of the neck before using liberally (especially on fair skin), and dilute them with almond, coconut, or another oil. Diluting with water only spreads and exaggerates the burning sensation. After using hot oils, immediately wash your hands.

Deciding which oils to use is a personal matter. Lavender oil is well-known for its calming properties, but I can't use it because it gives me a headache. Many individuals cannot tolerate undiluted peppermint oil on their skin, but I can. Aside from such personal propensities, many people consider frankincense, lavender, peppermint, and a high-quality muscle-relaxing blend to be the quintessential collection of headache-busting essential oils.

If you are pregnant, have asthma, high blood pressure, or other health issues, it is doubly important to research any oils you do not understand and check with a doctor who practices both holistic and conventional medicine. Be especially considerate of any pets—birds have no lungs, just air sacs, and are highly susceptible to airborne substances. Cats and dogs are vulnerable, too. Again, *always* wash your hands after using oils—especially hot oils.

Experiences with Essential Oils

I was face-down on a massage table the first time I experienced the benefits of essential oils. The massage therapist applied an unidentifiable liquid to my back and began to massage my ridiculously knotted muscles, which, astonishingly, relaxed immediately. "Wow! What did you put on my back?" I asked.

"That was an essential oil—a blend."

I bought a bottle and spread the word.

That's when I started taking classes to learn about essential oils, their therapeutic uses, and techniques like the Rainbow Technique. Rainbow amplifies the oils' benefits by layering them in a specific order. After building a body of knowledge and a collection of oils, I was able to help clients, friends, and family in need of healing. Eventually, strangers seeking relief benefitted from them, too.

One day as I entered a large department store, a cute lady at the customer service desk caught my eye when she lifted her hands to her temples and grimaced. She greeted me as I approached the counter.

"May I help you?"

"Do you have a headache?" I asked.

"Oh, yes."

I said, "I have oils."

"Oh," she said, "Are you returning them?"

"No, no. I mean, I have therapeutic oils in my purse, and I can help you with your headache. Want me to?"

"*Ohhhhh, pleeeease. Yeesssss,*" she said.

I put a few drops of peppermint oil and a calming oil on her wrist and suggested she breathe it in. Her relief was so evident that I mentally revisited the experience many times, sifting through the factors that eliminated her headache: the extension of care, kindness, setting the intention of healing, and the oils. For me, it was a fulfilling moment that provided additional information about healing headache pain.

The power of essential oils also revealed itself when a fair-skinned friend had a headache. When I put a few drops of peppermint oil on her neck, she quickly reported that it burned (not seriously). I quickly diluted it with almond oil. The lesson was clear: Be prudent when using essential oils because reactions can vary from person to person.

Another lesson in caution came when I discouraged mice by saturating cotton balls with peppermint oil, then strategically placed them throughout my tool shed. My cat was attracted to the aroma and was in the shed for four hours before I discovered him. His eyes and nose were running horribly, and he developed respiratory problems that affected him for several years. (He eventually recovered, and is okay now, thank goodness.) At the time, I did not understand how my pets might be affected. I should have done my research and locked the door so no animals had access to the shed.

Many times, I have rubbed the base of my skull, neck, and shoulders with peppermint oil layered with a calming blend. The cool burn distracts me and disarms the headache while the calming oil reduces tension.

One of my godsons, Morgan, visited me one day when he wasn't feeling well. I made a concoction of hot tea laced with local honey, fresh lemon juice, a drop of frankincense, and two drops of a spicy oil blend. He called the next day and swore the drink had cured him. I took note.

I keep a bottle of my favorite oil in my purse and an oil-laden cotton ball in my car. No matter what happens as I go through my day, when I step into the car, the scent lifts my spirits. Keeping my oils handy also allows me to help others with headaches.

While some oils serve as a direct healing force, it's hard to beat the pleasure of brownies seasoned with peppermint oil or water flavored with orange or lavender oil. I sacrificed several pitchers of water before learning that one drop goes a long way.

My collection of essential oils telegraphs a healthy message to me. Just seeing the bottles on my shelf reminds me that I can, and do, take care of myself, and their fragrance creates an intoxicating atmosphere of peace.

#8

MASSAGE

Speak softly, I am getting my massage.

Theodore Roosevelt *(probably)*

Massage is always an act of self-care, but when a headache is present it can provide a healthy dose of relaxation and reset one's system—mind, body, and spirit. Of course, if a person were to hop off the massage table and run right back into the stress of overdoing, the benefits could quickly dissipate. Even so, massages promote good health by training the body to relax. They also fill a basic need for touch—a factor we literally cannot live without.

Massage types should vary as much as the individuals who receive them. Some people prefer a light touch, while others respond best to deep tissue work or a combination of methods. Regardless of style predilections, it is important to communicate your preferences to your massage therapist: "That's the perfect pressure," or "That's a bit too hard." When choosing a deep tissue massage, the pressure shouldn't make you want to jump off the table, rather it should be just under your threshold of pain—a good hurt. Because massage therapists work on a lot of body types, they appreciate feedback. They prefer that you communicate your needs and preferences, rather than never come back, or worse, never try massage again.

Muscle and connective tissue are encased by an amazing interconnected sheath called *fascia*. Fascia is like a transparent, fibrous bag that surrounds muscle, tissue, tendons, ligaments, and cartilage. The chemistry of negative thoughts, certain foods (discussed in the *Food* chapter), a lack of water, and over-exercising can cause fascia to stick to muscle and tissue. The result is the feeling that something has grabbed the muscle with iron fists and will not let go. Even tiny scalp muscles can grab. It's almost impossible to stretch muscle while the fascia is holding it hostage. Massage therapists know how to release fascia and free muscles, making the body more flexible and less prone to headaches.

All massages are beneficial, but tight bodies can require deep therapeutic methods to release fascia. A *gentle* touch can also result in muscles magically letting go, but such experiences occur at the hands of angelic bodyworkers who are in a category all their own. These dedicated therapists are, of course, worth locating.

Massage therapists possess different personalities and skills, so it's wise to try a variety of bodyworkers until you find a good fit. When calling a massage therapist, explain your status. Tell them if you are new to massage, and tell them if you're nervous. Ask which massage options are available. Therapeutic? Intuitive? Would you prefer a male or female therapist? Just say, "I have never had a massage, and I would like to ask you a few questions, but I don't know which questions to ask." The therapist will be happy to provide information and customize a session for your comfort and needs. You may also enjoy adding hot stone therapy to your massage (see the *Heat* chapter).

The first time you lie under the sheets on a massage table, you may feel a bit apprehensive, but by your third visit, any self-consciousness will probably have vanished, allowing you to sink further into the benefits of massage therapy. Professional massage therapists behave with high standards of personal privacy and integrity (if you're modest, it's okay to wear your underwear).

Every healing modality, including massage therapy, increases one's understanding of the relationship between the mind and body, so don't hesitate to schedule a massage. Schedule two. Let yourself rest a while. And remember to use simple massage methods at home—rub your feet, roll your back against a fence post, or let a spouse or trusted friend provide a relaxing massage.

Experiences with Massage

My education in anatomy and physiology helped me understand the benefits of massage and therapeutic touch. As I increased my knowledge through massage workshops, I was better able to encourage healing in myself, family, friends, and clients.

I have been the recipient of many massages. My appointments last an hour and a half because when my muscles are tight, even the burliest massage therapist has to work hard to address the deep layers of muscle and tissue. Several therapists have said, "*Wow!* You have a *really* high pain threshold," to which I mumble, "Mmm-hmmm . . . press harder, please."

Hundreds of massages saved me from mean headaches. By hundreds, I mean high hundreds, because the complex collection of elements that contributed to my headaches required copious amounts of bodywork. I didn't drink enough water. I didn't resolve the emotional wounds I had closeted away in my mind and physical body. I didn't get enough sleep or otherwise take care of myself. I exercised like a fiend. I had not learned to speak up appropriately. The perfectionist's "not good enough" tape ran like a tumultuous river beneath the surface of my life, and its adverse mental messages kept a pot of poisonous headache stew simmering on the stove of my being and manifested in my tissues. Unaware, my behaviors remained the same, and I ate a dose of that toxic stew on a daily basis. The combination of headache-related factors made finding solutions tricky, but through extreme effort, over time, answers materialized. Through it all, massage was a supportive respite and an act of self-love.

Every type of massage helped me, although some were more beneficial than others. The list includes deep muscle, therapeutic, polarity, cranial-sacral, Thai, body integration, Rolfing, hot stone, float, and others. I have laid on tables where therapists waggled my legs; some got on the table with me and pushed with their body weight. Some bodyworkers dug deep, while others used a light circular touch.

One massage included two therapists at once. I also learned how to use self-massage contraptions. My mind went on journeys into outer and inner space while I fell asleep on the massage tables of caring, experienced massage therapists. The connection between my massage therapists and me was spiritual and relieved my body, my mind, and countless headaches.

At a massage school in Santa Fe, I met a talented bodyworker named Gabriel. During our first appointment, he told me he "preferred to work on people for hours." He wasn't kidding (and he wasn't flirting). After that first massage, we scheduled appointments at my house so he could deliver those longer massages (one lasted over three hours). The extended massages were heaven-sent and relieved my wracked body and stressed psyche.

One of my favorite massage therapists, Kristen, once used a technique I had never experienced: hair pulling. She swooped my hair into her hand and twisted it to a point of tension where it met my scalp. Then she held it. And held it. And held it.

At least three minutes went by before she spoke. "Wow. Do you feel the *heat* coming out of your head?"

"No."

"Put your hand up here."

The top of my head felt like it had been parked by a furnace. It was shocking to realize I could be unaware of such an obvious sensation. Was this intense heat a case of too many brain cells firing in too many directions for too long? Tiny muscles grabbing? The relief she brought me improved the clarity of my mind and attitude and left me with a relaxed body and sense of peace.

On one occasion, I was in charge of a high-end wedding in Santa Fe. It involved indoor-outdoor parties and a ceremony that was part Native American, part Jewish, part Buddhist. I had three weeks to wrangle the details into order and was often awake at three a.m., scouring spreadsheets filled with tasks that needed my attention. With so much pressure, stress moved into my head in the form of blistering pain.

I was working at the bride and groom's house one day when a friend commented on my headache, then pointed to a black leather massage chair. "Sit," she said. I sat. Thirty minutes later, my muscles were loose, and the headache had almost disappeared.

All forms of loving touch are therapeutic for me—a friend who holds my hand or gives me a hug. One friend rubbed my feet so beautifully that all the tension drained from my body. When my mother rearranged the curls in my hair, my whole being relaxed. Every experience and each form of touch revealed more information about the powerful relationship between mind, body, emotion, and spirit.

9

SIMPLE DEVICES

Simplicity is the ultimate sophistication.

Vincent van Gogh

Sometimes the simplest tools provide the most effective way to release the muscle tightness that accompanies headaches. My favorite devices are low-tech (not electronic) and are most effective when used in an atmosphere that supports focus and a sense of tranquility.

One useful tool is the cylindrical, hard foam roller. Rollers come in varying sizes, but eighteen to thirty-six-inch lengths are the most versatile. After strenuous exercise or physical work, chemicals like lactic acid can cause muscle lockdown; the foam roller loosens fascia and flushes lactic acid from the muscle. It can be used on the front, side, and back of the entire body: quadriceps, hamstrings, side-body, hips, calves, back, arms.

The goal is to lengthen the muscle fibers and increase circulation and flexibility. Large rolling movements, small back-and-forth movements, and anything in-between will do the trick.

The roller can also elongate pectoral muscles that have tightened due to repetitive forward flexion (too many hours leaning toward a computer screen, for example). To stretch the pecs, lie on the roller vertically, from tailbone to head, knees bent, feet on the floor, and outstretch your arms horizontally. The weight of your arms will automatically lengthen the connective tissue in the shoulder girdle. You can improve your body alignment by performing this easy maneuver every day. (Posture has a major impact on headaches.)

The massage stick is another crafty self-massage device. It looks like a rolling pin covered with sections that rotate as they move across muscle fiber. You can use the stick yourself or hand it off to a trusted friend who can roll out hard-to-reach muscle groups.

Small specialty balls are invaluable for their ability to release knots near the shoulder blades, hips and other areas of the body. Yoga Tune Up Therapy Balls are an excellent choice for this purpose because they are made of a specialized rubber that slightly grips the skin and allows them to affect multiple layers of muscle. These therapeutic balls measure 2-1/2" in diameter and come in a mesh pouch that fits easily into a backpack, large purse, or carry-on suitcase for travel. You can find Yoga Tune Up Therapy and other therapeutic balls on *www.TheHeadacheMystery.com*.

Yoga Tune Up Fitness balls, and tennis and lacrosse balls convert into handy massage devices when inserted into the toe of a long-necked cotton sock. Place the ball-sock massager on a wall or doorframe, and lean into it, gently moving side-to-side over the ball. This exercise is particularly suitable for the jaw, shoulders, and the area between the scapulae and the spine.

Additional pressure can be applied by lying on the floor and placing the balls in strategic positions—particularly the upper back, buttocks, hips, neck, shoulders, and, *ahhh*, the bottoms of the feet.

The scalp can benefit from using a head massager. Head massagers have a handle and bendable metal fingers that operate like a hand. You can also loosen scalp muscles by gently rolling the top of the head against the inside of a doorframe or wall. (Sounds weird, works well.)

Many ingenious self-massage devices can be found in health-related businesses such as health food stores and massage studios. They can be ordered online, of course, but in-person shopping allows you to examine them before you buy. I was introduced to therapy canes and "whopper-balls" in a massage studio in Asheville, North Carolina. My spring-loaded whopper ball uses a whipping motion to deliver a beneficial "bop" to my upper shoulders and back (fun to use).

The curved design of a therapy cane uses leverage to massage the upper back and allows the user to control the pressure (very cool). Even a rocking chair with a back made of vertical round spindles can provide an excellent massage to the back and scapulae—so can an out-facing corner where two walls meet. (Picture a bear rubbing against a tree.)

A soft rope knotted at each end makes an excellent tool for stretching tight pectoral muscles. Merely grasp both ends of the rope, then reach forward with straight arms, and slowly swoop your hands up and over your head, continuing the motion in an arc downward behind you; then pause, take a breath, and gently reverse the movement, slowly bringing the rope back over the head to starting position. Repeat the exercise seven times slowly while breathing deeply.

The tools you use to loosen muscle and fascia will work best when you replace stressful thoughts with images of love, gratitude, and beauty. Remember to hydrate, breathe deeply, and picture each muscle relaxing like warm, melting butter.

Experiences with Simple Devices

I discovered foam rollers and Yoga Tune Up Therapy Balls at a YMCA in Asheville and learned how to use them during *Stretch and Release* sessions taught by one of the best athletic trainers I know.

When I shopped for a foam roller, the broad selection of roller types was daunting. The roller I purchased was based on the advice of a Marine who happened to be standing beside me in the exercise section of the store. He pointed to a roller with smooth knobs on its surface and said, "That's the one we use." That's the one I bought.

When I use the roller, I put a yoga mat on the floor, then gently lean back until my scapulae rest on the cylinder. After I'm comfortable, I slide up and down twenty-five times. Next, I sit on the roller and gently rock one hip at a time across the knobs. To stretch my quadriceps, I rest the front of a thigh on the roller and crawl forward (forearms flat on the floor). As I slide across the cylinder, I let the knobs press into the muscle—it hurts in a good way. I moderate the pressure by counterbalancing my weight with my forearms.

After using the roller, I use Yoga Tune Up Therapy Balls to work through my neck, scapulae, and any tight spots on my back and hips. Because proper technique is imperative, I take classes with knowledgeable people and use online videos from reputable sources. (Training videos are available on the Tune Up Fitness Worldwide website.)

"Wall massage" has become a favorite relaxation method—I put the top of my head against a wall and roll it around (gently) to loosen tight scalp muscles. To release my upper back, I press my trapezius muscles into an outward-facing corner where two walls meet or roll them across the vertical spindles on the back of my rocking chair. I also keep my homemade sock massager in my car. It comes in handy on long drives and is a fun conversation piece for any passengers.

#10

REFLEXOLOGY

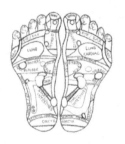

*Learn how to see. Realize that
everything connects to everything else.*

Leonard da Vinci

The feet are maps of the body. From heel to toe, nerves and meridian pathways in the foot relate to the organs and elements that comprise our physical bodies. The practice of reflexology is related to acupressure but primarily uses pressure points on the feet. The big toe is associated with the head and is especially important for headache release. The sides of the big toe correspond to the neck, which also affects headaches. Following the curves of the foot, one can identify all structures in the body, and because most people can reach their feet, reflexology is an easy way to accelerate healing. It is definitely a modality worth learning.

The technique most commonly associated with reflexology involves a specific type of rubbing movement, usually performed by the thumb. "Finger-walking" can be learned in hands-on classes or on reliable internet sites. Massage therapists and essential oil practitioners often teach reflexology workshops. You can also experiment by using common sense and applying pressure intuitively.

One advantageous reflexology technique is to gently rotate the big toe in both directions until it feels loose. After loosening the big toe, scoot the thumb or fingers toward the adjacent toe—where the big toe and the second toe meet the foot. Massage any tender spots. Look for sensitive areas on all of the toes—these are often the reflexology points that relieve headaches. The space between the big toe and the second toe is often tender due to blocked energy flow, and although rubbing it can be painful, the benefits quickly become self-evident. If the right side of the head hurts, rub the left foot, and if the headache is on the left side, rub the right foot—or both.

A pedicure provides some of the advantages of reflexology and carries the added benefit of immersing the feet in warm water. The warmth increases blood flow in the lower extremities, reducing pressure in the head. Home pedicures can relieve headaches as easily as salon pedicures and are sometimes *more* effective because they redirect the mind toward a positive mental focus and require stretching the hip flexors (reaching for your feet loosens the ligaments and tendons where the femur angles into the hip socket). Relaxed hips also help you heal your headache.

Keep in mind that the hands also possess pressure points and provide an alternative method to using reflexology on the feet. Whether you choose to activate pressure points on the hands or feet, reflexology can help you say goodbye to headaches and hello to *ahhh*.

Experiences with Reflexology

My first job was working for a state senator. One day his wife came to the office when my head hurt so badly I was green. Literally, pale green. The senator's wife took me home, put me on a bed in a darkened guest room, and rubbed my big toe for half an hour. At first, the pressure hurt (a lot), but the pain lessened as she continued to rub. She eventually tiptoed out of the room, saying, "You just stay there with your eyes closed." I remember how good the pitch-black room felt before I fell asleep. When I awakened, all signs of pain and tension were gone. Completely gone. That experience was my first foray into the world of reflexology and the awareness that headaches could be obliterated quickly. The encounter ignited a curiosity that helped me find my way back to health.

Eventually, reflexology workshops taught by Laurie, a talented essential oils coach, reflexologist, and massage therapist, provided me with the science behind reflexology and hands-on practice. Reflexology helped me ward off many headaches.

One particularly gruesome headache sent me running to a pedicurist in Longmont, Colorado. As the gentleman worked on my feet, he could see how much pain I was feeling and extended the massage portion of the pedicure. When I left, the headache was notably diminished.

The home pedicure earned my affection by repeatedly proving its capability to vanquish a headache. I attribute this success to the combination of reflexology, warm water, focus, and the accompanying stretched hip abductors required to reach my feet. A good old-fashioned home-style pedicure always diminished my head pain, relaxed my mood, and resulted in two good-looking feet, if I may say so myself.

11

MOVEMENT & EXERCISE

Leave all the afternoon for exercise and recreation,
which are as necessary as reading.
I will rather say more necessary because
health is worth more than learning.

Thomas Jefferson

Movement is movement is movement. It can be physical or mental, intentional or coincidental, tedious or fun; whatever the form, movement is productive and vital for wellness. For our purposes, we'll label movement as any activity that boosts us out of the realm of pain.

Physical exercise is well-known for building strength and improving cardiovascular health. It also activates the *yay-you!* hormones that generate a positive mental outlook. Even the act of putting on workout clothes and heading to the park or gym sends a signal that a choice for health has been made: *I am strong! I am healthy!* Physical exercise affects every organ and system within the body. It's indispensable. In a very real sense, exercise is the fountain of youth.

There are two general categories of traditional exercise: anaerobic and aerobic. Both types benefit fitness and mental health.

Anaerobic workouts are fast-moving activities, like jumping, that quickly deplete the body's oxygen supply. We can only jump for a short time before becoming winded. We know we're in anaerobic mode when we're gasping for air.

Weight-bearing exercises are also anaerobic, and are beneficial because they strengthen muscle and bone while tightening the entire body. Free-weights, resistance bands, and weight machines are excellent ways to increase strength and stability, but you can also obtain terrific results without ever picking up a barbell. Yoga, walking, and other exercises use the weight of the body instead of equipment.

Aerobic exercises develop stamina and heart health. They also boost endorphins that modify the perception of pain—invaluable for headache-prone people. These workouts involve activities that are well-paced and balance oxygen intake with the body's demand. Walking, dancing, jogging, and snow skiing are aerobic. If we can hold a conversation while exercising, we know we are in aerobic mode.

Some of the most beneficial forms of movement have nothing to do with conventional exercise or working out. Emotional and sensory movement are important, too.

Picture yourself in a boat, moving across a glassy lake in the early morning. Feel the wind on your face. Catch the fragrance of piney woods. How do you feel? *What* do you feel? Free? Relaxed? Grounded? Okay, maybe you don't have a boat. But you don't need one because you can generate similar benefits in an assortment of ways. A drive in the country brings the smell of new-mown hay, wildflowers, and unexpected adventure—a bigger world. Most cities have quiet parks for nature walks. You may choose to ride a bike, sweep the steps, organize a closet, or paint the front door. The point is to *do* something that escorts you out of the den of misery caused by head pain into new perspectives.

Humans have enormous mental capacities, but we have to keep an eye on our minds because they can get stuck in a rut—like a needle playing a vinyl record on a turntable. If the arm doesn't lift automatically, we have to manually raise the needle from the groove. The same thing happens with our minds and bodies, only it's not always easy to lift the needle. But you can do it, and it's well worth the effort.

Anything that improves the mind, body, or emotions is healing. Every proactive thought, word, and action moves us further from our dungeons of pain and closer to freedom from headaches.

Keep your body and mind fit. Keep moving. Do something healthy and new. Let movement lead you to new health, habits, and perspectives.

Experiences with Movement and Exercise

My mind can be very clever and busy. If I don't give it something useful to do, it starts dissecting my life, *your* life, and the world's problems. It fiddles with worrisome issues as if they are loose teeth.

Even after years of practice, I regularly catch myself staring at some grimy past experience. That's when I force a change in my thinking, and my world improves. Immediately. The easiest way I can switch my thoughts is to move physically. That's what a car ride to nowhere does for me. It shifts my mindset so I can see things in a different light—get some new

49

ideas. By the time I return home, I have usually discovered something important, like the need to get out more, make an overdue phone call, or eat healthier food. I may have a better understanding of why I talk so much. Maybe I'm compelled to finally rid myself of that heartbreaking old sweater my high school boyfriend gave me twenty years ago. All of these actions involve some form of movement and advance my quest to regain good health and happiness.

Whenever I had a headache, nothing else existed. I was in hell and didn't know how to get out. But as I approached my fortieth birthday, a lot of natural movement came my way. My eldest brother died. I became divorced. I changed my lifestyle and moved away from the familiar geography and culture that raised me. I loaded up my red jeep with blue jeans, artwork, tuna fish, crackers, water, and a portable CB radio, and charted a course for the great, unknown West. All of a sudden, I could think clearly. The massive changes were required for my well-being and growth.

During the same journey, I visited a friend in Arizona. On the first day, I was buried in a disabling headache. All I could do was sit on Willa's sofa, hold my aching head, and take pain pills. Willa finally said, "I think you need to go for a walk."

"Even with a headache?"

"Yes," she said. "*Especially* with a headache."

I walked slowly, but my friend was right. Moseying replaced my focus on suffering with a much larger world: wind, birds, sunshine, flowers, the sound of neighbors conversing. Those signs of life reminded me of options outside of headaches. The headache didn't go away, but it diminished significantly. The experience taught me about my tendency to become stuck and showed me a way to get unstuck.

Exercise is a significant mover and shaker for me. Some days I feel like I have lead in my blood; regardless, I go to Zumba or for a bike ride. I always come home with a refreshed view and ramped-up endorphins. Exercise also strengthens the core muscles that support my body's alignment—another factor that keeps headaches at bay. When I don't want to physically push my body, I walk down to the bay and watch the seagulls and pelicans soar. Such outings are mandatory for my mental health.

During my competitive athletic days, my emphasis was on mastering a sport, not physical fitness. Bodily conditioning was a side product of my efforts. I never thought about the energy expenditure because my attention was on perfecting my form (karate, dance, tennis). Sports added an element of fun and taught me about determination, dedication, and how to meet a challenge—all traits that supported me in my search for solutions to headaches. Each sport kept my body strong and put a spring in my step.

There have been many times when my world became very small and narrow as if I were a horse wearing blinders. Whenever I get that boxed-in feeling, I go for a hike, call a friend, exercise, write in my journal, or get in my car and drive. Sometimes I iron shirts, polish my desk, or wash the car—anything that constitutes change and improvement.

12

STRETCHING

*Arise from sleep, old cat, and with great
yawns and stretchings, amble out for love.*

Kobayashi Issa

Humans are exquisite machinery, and, like cars, we need proper maintenance to keep our gears running smoothly. In the world of physical conditioning, muscles are a vital cog in the mechanism.

When muscle tissue contracts, a natural change in pressure affects the nerves and blood vessels that oxygenate the brain and body. Prolonged constriction amplifies headache pain; elongation reduces it. That's why stretching is crucial. It's imperative, however, to stretch properly, because it's possible to *overstretch* and make matters worse.

Muscle tissue contains specialized cells called muscle spindle fibers. These fibers elongate and realign when stretched. However, if they are stretched *quickly*, they fire and *tighten* muscle tissue. This is why bouncing is forbidden when stretching—the jerky motion activates the spindle fibers and contracts the muscle. In particular, an improper hamstring stretch can impact the neck and lower back, contributing mightily to headaches. Fortunately, the neck, lower back, and backs of the ankles (Achilles tendons) mirror each other— stretching one area frees the other two, offering an effective way to diminish head pain.

Stretching should be a restful endeavor. Stretch as if you are Yoda or a baby sloth. Instead of bouncing as you stretch the hamstrings, for example, position the body for the stretch, take several deep breaths, and gently lean forward until the muscle feels slightly taut. Rest in that position and breathe, saying to yourself, *It's okay to let go*. Talk to the muscle. Picture relaxation going deep into your joints; envision the tendons and ligaments letting go. Notice how good it feels to relax. For added benefit, gently come out of the stretch, take a relaxed, deep breath, then slowly lean in again. Each additional stretch slightly increases the length of your muscles.

For headache relief, the hip is one of the most important areas to stretch. A simple hip stretch can be accomplished by sitting in a chair and putting one foot flat on the floor and placing the other ankle horizontally on top of the knee. After taking several deep breaths, lean forward until a little tightness expresses itself in the hips, then stay in that position while breathing deeply into the joint. Repeat the exercise on the opposite side. The same hip stretch can also be performed effectively while lying flat on the floor. Instead of keeping a foot on the floor, the shin will be raised to a ninety-degree angle, while the hands support the back of the lifted thigh.

As always, be gentle, taking care not to overstretch the sciatic nerve.

Alleviating tension in eye muscles can also relieve a headache. To lengthen and relax these small but powerful muscles, one can simply roll the eyes upward to the twelve-o'clock position (eyes open or closed) as far as possible, then *s-l-o-w-l-y* roll them counterclockwise several times before reversing the direction of the roll. (Take your time.)

Another method of stretching eye muscles is to roll the eyes upward to the twelve-o'clock position until a stretch is felt (remember to breathe), then bring them straight down to the six-o'clock position. When ready, roll them to 11 o'clock, stretch and hold, then roll them straight across to 5 o'clock. Continue traveling back-and-forth around the numbers on an imaginary clock, then rub your hands together and place them gently over your eyes for a soothing rest period.

Many factors affect tight muscles and fascia, including dehydration. A healthy diet is also imperative. Eat foods that support healthy fascia: leafy greens, garlic, berries, bell peppers, and tomatoes. Take care of your muscle tissue by using a foam roller or massage stick. Stay in tune with your body and heed its messages because something as seemingly harmless as high heels can shorten the hamstrings and initiate a headache.

Keep in mind that mental pain and physical pain often cause a constant state of constriction and bracing, even though the symptoms may be subtle. Remember to stretch during such times. If you are in a situation where you cannot physically stretch, use your mind and picture relaxing the joints and muscles as if you're in a dream. The imagination has a powerful effect on the body.

Experiences with Stretching

I studied sports science and psychology in college because I was fascinated with the interactions between the body, mind, and spirit. As an athlete, I lived in an agile body made for doing backflips and delivering vigorous karate kicks. It was fun to see what I could do, and my level of athletic function was high. I spent hours playing tennis and preparing for gymnastics tournaments. I was a ranked Black Belt, danced in a ballet company, and zoomed down tiers of concrete steps on rollerblades. I participated in innumerable advanced group exercise classes. I was determined and intense and too *busy* to associate my excessive habits with chronic head pain.

It took many years to realize how extreme physical activity without proper stretching (or water) made headaches worse. My body does best when I hydrate, warm up, engage in moderate exercise, rehydrate, then cool down and stretch for at least fifteen minutes.

On sparkling, clear days, I take walks or ride my bike. I feel so alive and happy when I come home that I sometimes don't stretch. The result is tension, so I make every effort to stretch and roll out my muscles even when I feel good.

On the rare occasion I wear high heels for an extended period, my hamstrings shorten and slide me toward a headache. I once walked to dinner in a gorgeous pair of gold wedge sandals, then traipsed around in the restaurant visiting friends. I wore the same shoes to a meeting the next day. Sure enough, the following morning, I awakened with a tight lower back, tight hamstrings, and a headache. Eventually, I stopped wearing heels.

One night I had a dream that awakened me with notable head pain, but instead of taking medicine, I got up (at two a.m.) and dedicated myself to slow breathing, stretching, and yoga. Afterward, the headache was completely gone. The experience reinforced my belief in using natural means to eliminate headaches. The incident also gave me a sense of control over my life and decreased my fear of head pain. I actually came out of that headache with a new Einsteinian equation: less fear equals less tension equals fewer headaches equals ever-expanding serenity and health.

13

BREATHING

Take a deep breath and tell us your deepest, darkest secret,
so we can wipe our brow and know that we're not alone.

Alan Watts

Watch a baby or puppy breathe and you will observe the ease with which the abdomen moves in and out. Indeed, breathing is effortless—until, that is, trouble appears on the horizon.

Let's imagine you are standing in five acres of daisies enjoying a happy-go-lucky afternoon when a T-Rex emerges from the woods at the edge of the field. The beast spots you and screeches nonstop as it runs toward you full speed, weird little arms flapping, monstrous spiked teeth glistening. Your lazy breathing snaps into *Save yourself!* mode as your brain issues orders to pump superhero chemicals into your body. All systems are *Go*, and your blood contains enough adrenaline to fuel Los Angeles for a day; you discover you can jump, run, and think at fantastic speeds. You escape by effortlessly leaping a fifteen-foot chasm. Hooray! But here's an interesting fact: if you had rolled over and played dead (and survived) instead of running, those fear chemicals would have blasted their way into your system anyway. It wouldn't have mattered if your body was running or still, because the self-protective fight or flight mechanism would have still wreaked havoc on your psyche. This response is especially pertinent in our speed-driven age of technology. It's the pressure and constant interruption that keeps the *Run!* instinct flashing in the background (or foreground) of the mind.

Enter deep breathing.

Deep breathing automatically signals the release of the body's natural calming system, delivered through the same mechanism that initiates the alert system. Our *interpretation* of an event determines which chemicals the brain distributes into the blood: freak-out or relax. Let's face it. Humans sometimes react like there's a rattlesnake in the house when it's just a drippy faucet; it is the *perception* of danger that sets off the alarm that starts the reactivity of fear-based chemicals, even when no danger is present. That kind of baseline tension is a setup for headaches.

A simple way to check someone's psycho-emotional state is to ask the person to take a deep breath. The shoulders will usually rise upward as the lungs take in a nip of air. A nip. If the goal is to relax body, mind, and spirit, breathing must occur slowly and deeply—from the diaphragm. A caveat for the person with an active headache: a deep breath sometimes exacerbates pain. At such times, one must do what is required to reduce the headache (ice, foot rub, salt bath, massage, stretch), then practice breathing properly when the headache subsides. Like this:

- ෧ Sit in a straight-backed chair sized so your feet are positioned comfortably and flat on the floor.
- ෧ Place a clear, pure glass of water within reach.
- ෧ If you wear glasses, take them off.
- ෧ Gently place your hands palms-down on your thighs.
- ෧ Slowly roll your shoulders forward, up, and back in a circular motion three times, then let them settle.
- ෧ Ensure that your head is balanced over your shoulders.
- ෧ Close your eyes.
- ෧ Observe the muscles in your shoulders, neck, and arms. Focus. Each time you notice tension, take a breath deep by extending your abdomen and picture the tightness releasing. Let go.
- ෧ Relax your tongue. Take your time.
- ෧ Take a deep breath. Take two more breaths.
- ෧ Tune into your jaw muscles. Let them release.
- ෧ Relax your eyelashes. Take your time.
- ෧ Relax your lips.
- ෧ Take three breaths slowly. Deeply.
- ෧ Now, just sit.
- ෧ Put one hand on your stomach just below your navel. Notice how the stomach moves outward when you breathe in, expanding to maximize space for oxygen intake to the lungs.
- ෧ Keep your hand on your stomach and become aware of the air and space surrounding you. Expand your awareness to the room, your yard, the city, the country, the world, and beyond. Focus on the air surrounding your miraculous body. The world is large. Think of the many places and ways to live that differ from your

current life. You are exactly where you are supposed to be, and yet you have innumerable choices.

- Return your hand to your thigh.
- Take a long, deep breath. Feel the air entering your nose and follow it down your throat. Notice how the temperature of the air changes as it travels downward.
- Observe your front and back ribs moving outward. As the air nears the diaphragm, the body fills like a balloon.
- Notice how your stomach, muscles, and ribs adjust as the breath shifts from breathing in to breathing out. Take three breaths. Ten breaths.
- Continue to observe gently breathing in and out.

Whenever you detect tension in your mind and body, take five minutes to breathe into your abdomen. Practice slowly counting to four during each inhale and each exhale. Breathing with intention releases a soothing neurotransmitter, gamma-aminobutyric acid (GABA) into the body. Eventually, just *thinking* the word "breathe" will initiate a tranquilizing deep breath.

An abbreviated breathing technique is to close the eyes and breathe slowly through the nose as if sipping air through a straw—then purse the lips and breathe out, slowly expelling as much air as possible.

Breath is the gift of life—the gift of trees and oceans. In their magnificent exhales we are given the oxygen that sustains us; in our exhales they receive a reciprocal gift of life. It is a beautiful system and a loving image that reminds us to ground, rest—breathe.

Experiences with Breath

I was introduced to breathing techniques when I studied Jivamukti yoga. My instructor believed in heavy doses of chanting and pranayama (forms of breathing), and she taught a variety of techniques. That same deep breathing has helped me remain calm in challenging situations and sidestep headaches before they gain a toehold.

Singing in choirs also required managing my breath, and an acting coach taught me to use deep breathing to calm myself before performances. Acupuncturists and massage therapists provided insights into the physiological, emotional, and psychological benefits of breathing into the lower abdomen. I believed my teachers and practiced what they taught me—with notable results.

The deeper I dive into simple things like breathing, the more fascinating life becomes. One day, years after I had learned to breathe properly, I noticed how my *back* ribs move in and out with each breath. I was delightfully shocked: *How could I have missed something so basic?*

I once coached a chronically headachy personal trainer with a go-go lifestyle. The first time we met, I positioned him comfortably in a chair and said, "Okay, just relax and take a deep breath." I watched his muscular shoulders rise toward his ears while a teeny amount of air made its way into his upper lungs. We discussed, then practiced, deep breathing. After he had taken three good breaths, he opened his eyes (which were twinkling), and said, "Oh my gosh. I'm dizzy! I've never felt that before!" His face had softened its expression. He was energetic but calm, all because he took three proper deep breaths.

Most people I coach have to re-learn how to breathe. Once they master deep breathing, they use the technique to complement other exercises, physical and mental, that release headaches.

14

GROUNDING

I go to nature to be soothed and healed,
and to have my sense put in order.

John Burroughs

Unresolved events, stress, pain, and emotions can pelt us with thoughts that dart in our heads like a flock of scattering birds. Anything that stops that kind of whirlwind thinking is your friend. One of those friends is called *grounding*.

Most folks know that a grounding rod can attract lightning from the sky and reroute it into the earth. Grounding *ourselves* can be viewed the same way. We experience grounding when we shift from a mind and body racing at Mach 5 into a state of presence. This re-entry into a centered consciousness is familiar to those of us who have gotten lost on the way to a friend's house. "Did you say to turn on Strodivant Street?"

Our friend says, "I don't know *where* you are! Did you

pass a little church on the right? Cute little church with a round window on the front?"

Then comes the moment we feel foolish. "Church? I didn't see a church," and of course, when you turn the car around, you find it sitting in plain view. Where were we before? Somewhere with a far away mind. Now that we see the steeple, the irresistible round window, we are back; we are grounded in the moment.

A centered psycho-emotional state can be initiated by an act as straightforward as walking on the grass barefoot or leaning against a tree trunk. Animals love to lie on the ground—it's as if they gather strength from the terra firma.

The result of grounding is a calm presence that brings clarity in current time—no need to look back over one's shoulder to dissect the past, no need to lean forward to see around the bend in the road to the future.

Any activity that requires mental and physical focus or stillness can be grounding: plant flowers, color in a coloring book, play cards. Attune your self-awareness so that you recognize when you need to center yourself, then find a way to do it.

A prerequisite to grounding is taking a break from cell phones, televisions, and computers. Tech manufacturers design devices to be addictive, and we have to love our lives enough to give ourselves time away from incessant pings, beeps, and their soul-sapping control and intrusions. The silence may feel awkward at first, but any discomfort will soon be replaced with a sense of relief when you remember who you really are.

Consider sitting on top of a hill with some water and a peanut butter sandwich. Plant a garden. Do something novel that takes you out of your comfort zone and requires focus. Such activities empower us by clearing away mental debris. Only then can we can hear answers whispered from within.

Experiences with Grounding

One day my yoga friend, Angela, and I were discussing our lives when she suddenly stopped and said, "Heavens. You have *dandelion* brain!

My eyes widened. "What do you mean?"

"Like when you blow on a fuzzy dandelion—one thought multiplies into a thousand others! I've never seen anything like it. Let me show you something." I followed her inside where she showed me a heavy, smooth, white rock. Angela explained that she held it when she meditated or felt scattered. When I picked it up, I understood. The rock felt dependable, a weighty tether to the Earth. Soon, I had my own collection of large, round rocks.

My childhood was crammed with grounding activities. I spent a lot of time alone in nature, close to flowers and bees, and stringing pink and yellow four-o'clocks onto Bahia grass stems to make necklaces. The enormous live oak tree in our backyard provided the perfect, horizontal limb where I communed with breezes and bark, polished acorns, and read. The smooth branches of a mimosa tree, fragrant with pink blossoms, created a living sanctuary where I wrote poems with a yellow pencil. After a good storm, I couldn't wait to walk barefoot in street gutters still running with rainwater. These, and other childhood experiences in nature, were cornerstones in a foundation that built my strong sense of connection and confidence.

During the years my mother was dying, a friend expressed concern for me. "When your mother dies, I'm afraid you're going to float off into the stratosphere." He had a valid point. Thank goodness for my propensity to collect rocks and be outside because those earthy habits supported me during that rough time in my life.

My yard is now sprinkled with rocks I have gathered from snowy New Hampshire creek beds and the Colorado Rocky Mountains. (When I find a great one, it comes home with me.) And I'm like an animal when I hike, unable to resist lying on boulders warmed by the sun, or rocky outcroppings that overlook valleys.

Other activities that ground me are playing the piano, dancing, gardening, ironing, painting, playing chess, exercising, cooking, and polishing silver. All of them involve manual operations that demand mental focus and keep me from over-thinking.

#15

WRITING

A piece of writing is a dangerous thing,
It can change your life.

Tobias Wolff

The Artist's Way by Julia Cameron encourages the practice of writing every morning. Cameron calls these writings "morning pages." Morning pages, and other journaling habits, are well-known for the light they shine on innermost questions and answers. The two sentences we write about piddly matters like, "The window company's coming to look at the bedroom windows tomorrow. Must remember to get cat food," often blossom into ten pages about hidden issues related to headaches (or other dilemmas).

The act of writing *by hand* is an incredibly powerful way to bring clarity because it's an organic process that is at the core of grounding: the mind, connected to the soul and heart, moves the arm, which possesses a hand holding a pen that moves across a piece of paper that was previously a tree that grew in the ground. The unspoken association with trees and earth provides a sense of safety and nudges us from mental gymnastics to rootedness. The nature of writing with a pen or pencil is also curative because it demands a slower pace than a computer keyboard—besides, handwritten journals are tangible. You can touch them, smell them—hear the paper rustle as you turn each page.

Journaling unites thoughts and feelings and calls out previously undetected sentiments. Your pages can easily transform into an oracle. When at last, you put down your pen, you will behold a rendering of your true emotions and perspectives. Not only is such writing therapeutic, it frequently serves up a large dish of valuable insight. And, in case you are inclined to wriggle out of journaling because you aren't a writer—know this: it doesn't matter. Forget spelling and phrasing. Make squiggles if you like— just think and feel while you do it.

Another reason to journal is to create a record of your life. Happy times. Sad times. As your collection of booklets grows, you may notice that a journal's closure coincides with the end of one chapter of your life and the beginning of another. These markers offer clues that illuminate your path. You may even want to read your volumes later in your life. (You may want to burn them.)

Writing letters to someone you perceive as having hurt you can be invaluable in releasing painful emotions. It's normal to write and rewrite the letter before finding inner resolution, depending on the depth of the wound and the nature and importance of the relationship. Observe how each letter changes with each rewrite. The first draft may be a screaming *rant* executed in bold strokes: "Why you lousy, *dirty, rotten,* scheming, dumb #@!*N! How the !#%E@! could you do that!?" When you have finished writing the letter, read it, then rewrite it. Each rewrite will become clearer, less emotional, and more powerful. Keep rewriting until the letter is a true representation of your feelings and perspectives. Then read it aloud, possibly to a trusted friend or therapist. Refuse any temptation to mail the letter; the intention is to heal *you*, not pile hurt onto an already hurtful situation. If, after careful consideration, you wish to write and send a final version of your letter, you can choose to do so with clarity of purpose— or you can destroy it. Either way, you have helped yourself.

Writing is like going on a treasure hunt. Once the pen delivers the first clue, you will likely want to search for more because it feels so good to liberate emotions previously stuffed into the basement of your heart. Telling the truth may make you cry, but those cleansing sobs are the sound of energetic logjams being cleared from the river of your life. Once the old logs are removed, it's easier to keep the water clear of debris. Easier to let the river run free.

Experiences with Writing

My grandmother gave me a sky-blue diary on my eighth Christmas. Its cover featured a teenage girl with a ponytail, pen poised, journal in hand, contemplating what she was about to write. I thought it was the most wonderful present, and holding its blank pages filled me with anticipation about my future. During the passing years, I recorded the ups and downs of my young life.

That diary remains precious to me because it was my first. It still possesses fingerprints from my youth, and it lives on a shelf beside a collection of journals I have kept throughout my adult life. Each one is a good friend that can transport me back in time. The compilation may mean a lot when I'm elderly: *Oh, I had forgotten about that trip to Maine!*

I keep a dream journal on a nightstand beside my bed. When a dream rouses me from slumber, I am sometimes so sleepy I don't want to wake up to record it. I force my eyes open and write it down anyway because the details inevitably reveal things I need to see.

My life has been grand but not easy. Journaling and writing letters to dead loved ones helped move me toward emotional freedom. Somewhere along the line, I started purchasing inexpensive paper notebooks and painting the covers. As I painted and wrote in each journal, I noticed a pattern: the completion of each diary coincided with a shift in my life. Some stages required two journals. The images I painted on the covers were like messengers from my inner self, dropping hints about the phase to come.

Before I left on my midlife journey to the West, I painted two journals featuring a slice of a blackbird wing. I inscribed the first page of the first journal with lyrics from the song *Blackbird* by The Beatles: *Blackbird singin' in the dead of night, take these broken wings and learn to fly. All your life, you were only waiting for this moment to arise.* Like the blackbird, I needed to mend my brokenness and learn to fly; and I had certainly waited a long time for the right moment to arise—to be free. My intention was to give the second journal to a friend, but something told me to keep it. My initial journey lasted three months—exactly the time it took to complete both of the blackbird journals. Such "coincidences" became a way of life.

My journals are good friends, and whenever I hold one of them in my hands I am awed because I'm literally touching my life—all the good, bad, painful, happy, regrettable, and courageous moments. Trips to Europe, trips to the hospital, births, deaths, things I chanced, risked, won, lost, learned.

Amazement and a sense of gratitude prevail when I hold my life's representative in my hands: *My life! I have one! Just look at it!*

Countless notes and letters of greetings and thanks have traveled between family, friends, and me. A Native American friend, Cecelia, writes handwritten correspondence from her reservation in New Mexico. I am grateful she started the process because her handwritten letters and cards ground me. It's a delight to find a "real" letter in my mailbox and a joy to handwrite a reply to my friend.

I am big on apology letters. One such letter involved a friend named Sammie. It took twenty years, but an unfortunate truth about myself finally marched up to me one day and made an announcement: *You are not the loyal person you think you are! You behaved in the worst possible manner to Sammie. She wasn't wrong—you were!*

Ouch. The discovery of a monolithic egotistical streak had finally raised its ugly head. For days I drowned in vats of grief, embarrassment, and shame. When I recovered, I got down on my knees and apologized to Sammie in the form of a note in which I attempted to convey the level of my remorse. I told her I knew my behavior was surely unforgivable, but I wanted her to know how deeply I lamented my actions.

What happened afterward? First, I felt tremendously better about myself. A bonus came in the form of a note from Sammie thanking me for writing and inviting me to come see her when I was in town. Some people are full of love.

16

STILLNESS & MEDITATION

*Stop the words now. Open the window in the
center of your chest and let the spirits fly in and out.
The quieter you become, the more you are able to hear.*

Rumi

There is an exercise in the book *Full Catastrophe Living* by
Jon Kabat-Zinn, PhD that requires sitting down and doing
nothing. There's no answering the phone or doorbell, no
incessant *doing* or reacting to every thought (*Did I turn off the
coffee pot?*). Within five minutes, breathing deepens. Within
ten minutes, a sense of calmness takes over. Sit for fifteen
minutes and you'll want to stay in the peaceful, non-reactive
world you have created.

How *busy* we can be. How unnecessary our list of
whirling have-to's. The world is just fine, thank you, without
me (or you) hopping up every minute. The phone can go
unanswered (you'll live); the doorbell can keep ringing (still

alive; the person will go away); the coffee pot can stay on (so what if the coffee burns). If you give the *sit-and-stay* exercise a try, take time to notice how clear you feel afterward.

Our cultural habit is to complete a long list of tasks in a short time. We feel frantic to accomplish every item—until, that is, we take a second look at our self-imposed demands and realize we can easily eliminate half of them—or at least postpone them.

Whenever tension becomes noticeable, take five minutes to sit quietly. Do *not* get up. No matter what. If unresolved feelings surface, remain seated.

Stillness leads to the discovery that emotions do not kill a person; rather, they bring a sense of power and personal control. The resulting relief and confidence connect with the individual's interior world instead of the finger-pointing exterior world.

Meditation is known for its positive influence on the harried mind and distressed body. There are myriad forms of meditation, so it's easy to find a method that suits you.

Herbert Benson, MD, professor of mind-body medicine at Harvard Medical School, founder of the Benson-Henry Mind-Body Medical Institute at Massachusetts General Hospital, and founding trustee of The American Institute of Stress is the author of *The Relaxation Response*. Millions of copies of his book are read worldwide. The relaxation response counteracts the body's fight-or-flight mechanism by using mantras, a form of prayer.

In Benson's experiments, subjects were instructed to sit quietly, breathe regularly, and repeat a mantra mentally or verbally for ten to twenty minutes while pushing intruding thoughts aside. People who repeated the mantras for as little as ten minutes per day experienced reduced heart rates, lower stress levels, and slower metabolisms. The practice also lowered the blood pressure of subjects with high blood pressure. General oxygen consumption was reduced, indicating a restful body state. The immune system was strengthened, as was the duration and depth of sleep.

Eliciting the relaxation response involves nine steps, but Benson's book includes a four-step shortcut. Two of the steps are imperative: a mental device (a simple word, phrase, or activity to keep the mind from wandering) and a passive, open attitude. The end goal is to activate the parasympathetic nervous system, which initiates relaxation.

According to Benson's research, over sixty percent of all visits to healthcare providers can be traced to stress. That doesn't mean it's all in your head. Stress floods the bloodstream with epinephrine, norepinephrine, and cortisol, which exacerbate conditions like hypertension, insomnia, chronic low back pain, heart disease, stroke, and, of course, headaches.

Meditative states do not always require sitting still. Painting, gardening, driving, walking, and other activities can also provide quietude, resulting in joy and providing answers we can't hear when our minds are racing. The aim is to allow a sense of intrinsic presence to arise and put an end to ceaseless ruminating. We want to enjoy the current moment, not jump backward and forward in time, oblivious to where we are standing.

There are many excellent articles, books, and videos about the benefits of meditation. Participating in group meditation, yoga, and intentionally taking time to sit still or be creative restores homeostasis to the mind and body.

Quiet is, indeed, the key to health and finding answers known only to you.

Experiences with Stillness and Meditation

Sometimes I catch my mind and body buzzing with worry or busyness and have to make myself stop and sit. When my mind stops whirling, I find myself returned to the present moment: *Oh, yeah, that's right. This is me here, sitting on the steps. It's all I have to do right now. Boy, the sky is bright blue today!* Instead of "Scotty, beam me up!" the feeling is of being beamed *in*—grounded. All the crazy-making mental gyrations stop. (I prefer living without them.)

Sometimes when I stop rushing, my emotions give me a big "hello." I may cry, but purging emotional sludge is an activity I can't live without. Expressing feelings is like rinsing with rosewater after being covered in slime.

When I'm quiet, I put myself in control. Instead of reacting to other people and events, I let other people talk, think, act, come, go, work, play, and make decisions without me jumping in to guide them, advise them, direct them, save them, or teach them. *Hallelujah!* I don't have to play God. Suddenly, I am powerful and free to notice the awe contained in the red-tailed hawk circling my head. In this state, I enjoy my own company and don't need anyone's approval.

As an adult, I needed to understand truth outside the confines of my societal upbringing. I couldn't figure out how to follow my mother's directive to "just be yourself" because a part of me was always guarded against cultural judgments. As events unfolded in my life, I learned to tune in to my personal questions and answers. The solutions were not always easy, and the lessons certainly not without pain—for myself and others—but they marked my roadmap to happiness. That map led me to the Southwest.

My life in New Mexico and Colorado provided me with perspectives that allowed me to gradually dissolve the tension that had resided in me for so long. As I traveled through the desert (how appropriate), I began to notice how everything I needed came to me via my thoughts and actions. If I needed a place to live, one showed up. Out of the blue.

When I first arrived in Santa Fe, I took a temporary job at a resort. On my third day, a girl who worked in the office asked me where I was living.

When I told her, she said, "I have an apartment at my house in Nambé."

I said, "Seriously? That's so nice of you, Nan, but I'm not sure I can afford it. How much is the rent?"

"Who said anything about paying rent?"

Really? Yes, really. And in the end, divine intervention put us together for a good reason. I needed a place to live, and her six-year-old daughter needed someone who could build her confidence and teach her how to read—which happened to be my specialty. So in the end, we traded gifts.

My entire westward journey was a form of meditation because I was alone, driving through deserts, sitting solo on mountainsides. Listening. I was painting and journaling, too. Over time, I came to understand how events and people dropped into my life whenever I needed a guide for the next stage of my evolution. Each new awareness strengthened my resolve to act on the instructions of the voice within. That voice came to override all other voices.

I once undertook *A Course in Miracles,* a curriculum that ties spirituality to psychology. The course was originally written for Columbia University, but it turned out to be much more than the author intended. ACIM, as the program is fondly called, requires brief periods of meditation and has helped millions of people retrain their minds and behavior. The course takes a year to complete. A hundred and twenty-five people attended the first night of my ACIM course, and after we closed our opening session, one of the facilitators asked me how I felt. I told him I was excited. He waved his arm toward my classmates and said, "You see all these people? Most of them will never finish the course. I'll be surprised if a third of you are here in a year."

I didn't appreciate his doubt. "*I'll* finish it," I said. And I did.

Nowadays, I gather weekly with seven spiritually-minded friends to meditate and advance my knowledge of spiritual practices. Meditating with a group amplifies the benefits of my meditation practice and opens my heart and mind to ever-greater possibilities. I also walk alone in the woods and participate in meditative practices at yoga and at church.

I begin every day saying thank you for my life. I read from spiritual writings, pray, and sit outside with the cat as the birds sing darkness into daylight.

17

YOGA

Yoga is like a geologist for the soul;
it can show you where to dig, and what to dig for,
but the digging you must do yourself.

Rumi

A lot of people think yoga is putting the body into positions that build strength and flexibility. Those attributes are certainly a part of yogic practice, but yoga's real power lies in its ability to shift individuals into a state of peace and unify the body, mind, and spirit.

Yoga comes in a variety of forms, all of which provide excellent practices. Classes range from restorative to athletic styles. One type of yoga is not more desirable than another, but it is important to find classes that bring a sense of ease and meet your needs. The book, *Light on Yoga,* is the quintessential guide to yoga, and students are wise to obtain a copy.

Beginner yoga builds a solid foundation and develops proper form. Even advanced practitioners attend beginner classes because they sometimes discover that while they may be able to move from a one-legged full wheel (backbend) into a handstand, they have developed sloppy form in Mountain pose (standing still in proper alignment).

One of the merits of yoga is its ability to instill a sense of tranquility and calm—qualities helpful to folks interested in eliminating headaches. Yoga also builds a strong physical core. A strong core is necessary to maintain a healthy framework in the body—crucial for doing away with headaches.

No two bodies are the same, so modifications to yoga postures can mean the difference between a beneficial stretch and a permanent knee injury. A good instructor always teaches proper alignment while encouraging students to modify postures as needed. Both group and private yoga classes should provide personalized instruction regarding form, breathing, and modifications.

Yoga practices you may wish to investigate:

- Ⓔ **Hatha** yoga provides knowledge of proper alignment and postures, called *asanas*. Hatha is a gentle practice that induces a state of calm, lengthens muscle, and ensures proper form. Hatha yoga's slow pace accommodates all fitness levels.
- Ⓔ **Iyengar** yoga accentuates precise alignment, deep focus, timing, and breathing techniques that cultivate self-knowledge and keen awareness. Iyengar is a very grounding practice.
- Ⓔ **Restorative** yoga allows practitioners to rest in each pose. Props like blankets, straps, and bolsters supply comfort and support, and the spirit of restorative yoga is especially loving.
- Ⓔ **Kundalini** yoga focuses on freeing energy that collects at

the base of the spine (root chakra) while simultaneously building core strength. Some poses are advanced and require considerable effort, but the benefits can include amplified emotional release. Avoid Kundalini yoga unless you have an expert teacher because Kundalini energy is extremely powerful and must be managed wisely.

- ◎ **Vinyasa** yoga connects asanas in a sequential flow of movement that involves heightened breath control.
- ◎ **Jivamukti** yoga is a vigorous asana practice with a focus on developing compassion, oneness, and personal enlightenment while building physical strength.

A regular yoga practice can punctuate your life with peace. It cultivates an awareness of breathing and movement that identifies, then releases, tension. The increased relaxation fosters a life without pain—in or out of yoga class.

Experiences with Yoga

When I returned to my hometown to help my elderly mother, stress levels were high, and the frequency and intensity of my headaches accelerated. Help came in the form of a yoga studio four blocks from Mom's house. When I started my practice, I had no idea I was stepping into the world of Jivamukti yoga.

Each class began with prayer in the form of chanting led by our strong, dedicated teacher, Linda. After focusing on the chants, we practiced breathing techniques, then stood, toes near the front of our mats, hands to hearts, each of us privately setting an intention we would carry throughout the class. My exertions were usually dedicated to my mother, the environment, or my own healing. By the time the music began to play, I was already in a peaceful mental state.

As the class began to move through a series of asanas, I rapidly discovered where my body held tension. After the active flow of postures was completed, we lay in Savasana, a reclining pose where we rested before quietly rolling up our mats and donning our flip-flops.

My education in yoga eventually grew through participation in various class types, but Jivamukti yoga taught me the most, partially because I practiced it longer than any other kind of yoga. With time, I learned to let go deep within my body, which afforded enormous relief from headaches.

One lesson I learned in yoga was not to push myself too far. Because I was athletic, I over-performed every pose, especially when my teacher encouraged me (with the best intentions). I couldn't do bow pose or a full wheel (backbend) without hurting my back. I suspected my spine was out of place, but continued trying to do back-bending asanas anyway. I later discovered physical anomalies and sports injuries that prevented me from doing backbends. Turns out, I had been ramming bones together. Yoga was an object lesson about accepting limitations, the downside of being competitive, and the importance of listening to my instincts—even when they run contradictory to the advice of a valued teacher.

18

ACUPUNCTURE & ACUPRESSURE

The human body is the most intricate of all God's creations.
The power and extent of the consciousness that is
present in the body is beyond human conception.

Paramahansa Yogananda

Acupuncture is the ancient practice of strategically placing fine needles on specific points of the body with the goal of restoring energy and blood flow to a state of equilibrium. The tiny needles dispatch healing by way of a network of channels, or meridians, that run throughout the body. Acupuncture amends a broad range of complaints. It can ease nausea, boost the immune system, increase energy levels, encourage sleep, relieve pain, and more.

The needles used in acupuncture are so small that a good practitioner can insert them without the client ever feeling them. A needle may hurt a little if it touches a tight spot, but the doctor will happily adjust or remove it. I have had acupuncturists who suggested I allow a specific *type* of discomfort because of the release it can bring. The appropriate level of discomfort is very individualized—you will instinctively know if the needle needs to be adjusted.

Acupuncturists sometimes use a combination of methods to move energy. "Cupping," for instance, involves heating the air inside small cups before placing them on the body. The negative pressure inside the cup creates a suction that pulls toxins through the tiny capillaries connected to the skin. Cupping leaves a few red marks (you will look like you've been embraced by a large octopus), but the result is a state of heightened serenity and well-being.

Acupuncturists often complement treatments by using mugwort, an herb. Burning mugwort (moxibustion) increases heat therefore, blood flow, and feels similar to a hot stone massage. The body reacts with profound relaxation and a marvelously balanced system.

Community acupuncture offers excellent benefits and reduced treatment costs because the acupuncturist can simultaneously treat multiple clients. The treatment room is a large, peaceful area incorporating a circle of comfy recliners, cozy blankets, and soft light; it's so quiet you think you're the only one there. The acupuncture needles are inserted only on the front of the body—hands, feet, ears, for example, so clothes-wise, the only things you have to take off are your shoes. There's no rushing out the door, either—you can stay and rest as long as you like. (Heavenly.)

Acupressure is similar to acupuncture, except the practitioner uses the hands to communicate with the body's meridians—no needles. As always, research your therapist's experience, and follow your intuition when selecting a practitioner.

Experiences with Acupuncture & Acupressure

I have been to four professional acupuncturists, and every one of them relieved tension and pain. Sometimes, the acupuncture treatment totally eliminated what seemed to be an intractable headache. During such visits, if the needle caused a twinge, a mental focus on releasing my muscles usually dissipated the discomfort, leaving the needle to do its work in peace. If a needle felt *too* uncomfortable, I asked the doctor to adjust or remove it.

I was living in Santa Fe when a particularly unrelenting headache came upon me; it was so insidious I sought out an acupuncturist (my first) and crawled onto his table, trying not to move my aching head. The young man who tended to me was so concerned about me he called in his senior acupuncturist. Both practitioners worked on me for over an hour. Before I left, they taped a tiny metal bead onto a sleep meridian on each ear. I went home, lay down on the sofa, and slept the most profound sleep I had experienced since I was a baby. No exaggeration. I may have been drooling. When I woke up, my body and mind felt absolutely new—zero pain. My mind was clear, my body rested, and my emotions calm. The contrast between deep sleep and surface sleep was striking, and being pain-free was priceless.

The only unfortunate experience I had with acupuncture involved a treatment at an acupuncture school. I was aware that the school was a training ground. I also knew that some students would possess a natural gift for acupuncture; others, not so much. My student was in the not-so-much group, and, with all respect, I tell you the man was better-suited for packaging potatoes. I intuitively knew this when I met him. I even considered excusing myself: "You know, there's something that doesn't feel right for me. Maybe I'll come another time." Or, "Something's telling me I should see someone else." But due to my lingering habit of being overly "polite," I said nothing. Instead, I chose the fool's course and let him jab a needle into the third eye area on my forehead. I bled. The man had hands like sledgehammers and zero intuitive capability. I reiterate that I, being as empathic as a canary, was responsible for this unfortunate experience. It was one of the events that convinced me to follow my intuition, speak up, and take care of myself. (My silence probably didn't do the student any favors, either.) Obviously, my favorite acupuncturists are gentle, natural healers.

I discovered community acupuncture at Sunflower Community Acupuncture in Hygiene, Colorado. The clinic possessed an atmosphere of serenity and provided a peaceful timeout from the stresses I was experiencing. Because the physician was talented and loving, she ameliorated many of my headaches. Since community treatments were more affordable than private acupuncture sessions, I was able to visit Sunflower frequently.

19

CHIROPRACTIC

There is a vast difference between
treating effects and adjusting the cause.

D. D. Palmer

Chiropractic is a form of alternative medicine focusing on the diagnosis and treatment of mechanical disorders of the musculoskeletal system. Headaches are sometimes lessened or alleviated with chiropractic adjustments.

The methods chiropractors use to move bones range from physical force to gentle touch. One practitioner may use their hands to manipulate the body, while another may engage a padded pop-up table with Jack-in-the-Box parts that "bop" the targeted area. Some chiropractors incorporate small bolsters and wedges that encourage subtle changes in structure, requiring the patient to lie still while gravity does the work.

Muscle operates the skeleton via opposing muscle groups: one muscle (or group of muscles) shortens while the opposing muscles lengthen. This dynamic allows our bodies to move.

Because muscle operates bone and movement, it's important to identify which muscles need to be strengthened, and which need to be lengthened. Armed with such knowledge, a workout at the gym can support chiropractic adjustments instead of undoing them. Because elongated, flexible muscle makes manipulation easier, chiropractors often treat clients with massage therapy prior to making adjustments.

Sometimes chiropractic medicine moves beyond direct physical manipulation, as in the case of Network Chiropractic. "Network" involves gentle touch—no twisting or extreme adjustments. Its effectiveness is based on brain-spine connections, the innate self-healing nature of the body, and the use of touch to affect stored tension patterns that pull the spine out of position. Network bears an almost mystical quality and requires a trusting connection between practitioner and patient.

If you suspect your skeletal system is misaligned, insist on getting X-rays before allowing any manipulation of your body. Licensures, testimonials, and personal referrals help confirm credentials and the integrity of the chiropractor.

Experiences with Chiropractic

I have always had a problem with chiropractors because I don't like someone yanking my head around. When I finally learned to relax, I realized that, yes, I felt better after visiting a chiropractor. In particular, my headaches were lessened, and my vision was sharper (I still steer clear of chiropractors who use jerky methods).

Numerous encounters with a range of chiropractic styles resulted in some unusual experiences.

One doctor picked me up, flipped me sideways, and shook

me. His adjustments *always* helped. Another one used a pop-up table to make adjustments. Yet another doctor positioned me in a prone position, then teased out an adjustment by placing small wedges under one hip—all I had to do was lie still and let go. But my favorite chiropractor is the one who told me, "I wouldn't touch you with a ten-foot pole," then ordered X-rays. The X-rays revealed the extra piece of bone that had been floating near my spine since birth, which explained the range of movement problems I experienced in sports.

One sales-y chiropractor used high-pressure fear-based tactics: "If you buy fourteen sessions *today*, and *only* today, you'll *only* pay $2,400.00!" He pointed to my X-rays and shook his head. "See that?" (I had no clue how to read X-rays), "You're going to need surgery within the next two years." Even though I saw through his pushy behavior, this man had me so frightened that I drove home crying. Of course, I never went back. Fifteen years later—no surgery.

Because of my athleticism and studies in kinesiology, I understood body mechanics, so I also understood that a chiropractor might be able to rearrange my bones and relieve headaches, but if I went home and lifted a weighty pot of geraniums, my muscles would pull those bones back out of alignment. When I maintain a strong core, my muscles hold my skeleton straight and support the adjustments.

I stumbled into Network Chiropractic during the summer of 1992. Robin was a network chiropractor I met while visiting a friend. When Robin discovered I had a headache, she set up a narrow massage table and had me straddle it as if I were sitting on a horse. Then she sat behind me, wrapped her arms around me, and matched the rhythm of her breathing with mine. As I relaxed into the joint breathing, I was whooshed away as if I were traveling in my dreams. I was *gone*—traveling to the moon gone. When I returned to a state of wakefulness, I was utterly tranquil, and all I remembered was that I had howled like a wolf (not out loud).

The headache was nowhere to be found.

#20

ENERGY HEALING

Reiki is love,
love is wholeness,
wholeness is balance,
balance is well being,
well being is freedom from disease.

Miako Usui

Humankind was understandably awestruck when the atom was discovered invisibly humming through our world and beyond, and we continue to be amazed as scientists unravel additional wonders. When researchers look deep into an atom, all they find is empty space with particles. Open one of the particles and, *voilá!*—more empty space, more particles. To stand at the center of an atom must be like looking at an endless night sky sparkling with stars. For some, as it does for me, such findings open the mind to exciting possibilities for healing.

Energy healing is a form of health restoration that fine-tunes the invisible, atomic vibrations that permeate the physical body. Like starlight, our bodies zing with energy that extends outward from the smallest cell to beyond our skin. Energy practitioners refer to these fields as subtle bodies, or biofields—sometimes called auras. Like all elements of a human being, these energies are affected by experiences, thoughts, and emotions. Health, it seems, travels from the inside out *and* the outside in, with no barrier separating the two.

Awareness of the body's energy fields and their relationship with health isn't a new concept. Eastern cultures have practiced energy healing for thousands of years (India, China), and current scientific research provides us with additional insight into those ancient practices.

In 1911, Walter Kilner, MD, measured changes in human energy fields relative to shifting frames of mind. In conjunction with Kilner's work, Dr. Valerie Hunt recorded signals from electrodes placed on people undergoing Rolfing (deep massage). The scientists used Kirlian photography to correlate frequencies with the colors of the body's energy centers, or chakras. Their research revealed that when participants were exposed to pleasant circumstances, a colorful corona expanded around them, but the colors almost disappeared during extreme stress. They correlated constricted energy fields with unhealthy conditions. Those conditions could be dispelled *before* they had time to manifest in the dense body.

In his article, *Energy Healing Comes Into the Light*, Deepak Chopra, MD (with Tiffany Barsotti, MTh, and Paul Mills, MD) references a study that tracked chronic fatigue in breast cancer survivors: ". . . findings showed that study participants who received energy healing over a four-week period had statistically significant and clinically relevant reductions in their chronic fatigue . . . In addition, the healing-energy group showed a significant restoration in their daily levels of the hormone cortisol, which is typically flattened in chronically fatigued breast-cancer survivors." Physicians like Chopra continue to search for mechanisms utilized by biofields.

Energy is our life force, and it's important to keep it clear of debris. Energy healers aid the process by facilitating the body's innate ability to return to a state of balance and health.

Reiki and Pranic Healing are modalities in which the practitioner directs universal energy in and out of the body. These methodologies create balance by removing blocked energy from the body (stored emotional energy attached to the self, other people, and the past), and increasing energy in areas that are deficient.

In Polarity Therapy, the practitioner uses the hands to connect with specific points on the client's body, creating a circuit that opens blocked electrical pathways. The patient's breathing cues the timing of the therapist's movement around the body.

In choosing the right Reiki, Pranic Healing, or Polarity Therapy practitioner, look for qualities of trustworthiness and a giving nature. Check in with your intuition. While universal energy does the healing, it's important for the facilitator to fully understand the process. Our healing is, after all, sacred.

Reiki, Pranic Healing, Polarity Therapy, and other forms of healing touch are powerful tools to keep in one's health toolkit; anyone can learn to use them. If you decide to study energy medicine, find a knowledgeable, intuitive teacher.

Cords are invisible attachments that result from interactions that occur throughout your day. Even *thinking* about an event, person, or place can create a subtle attachment, an invisible cord. A simple way to improve your overall state of well-being is to intentionally cut these energy cords. Disconnecting ourselves in this way provides an objective space that brings great relief, and the method is easy to do.

Every morning and night, anytime you need to gather a sense of self, set an intention to let go of everyone and everything. (The love between people, places, and things always remains intact so you can discard any apprehensions related to loyalty.) To "cut the cords," flatten your hand, fingers touching, and picture it surrounded by brilliant blue and white light. Keep this image in your mind and use your hand like a knife to cut the invisible cords surrounding your body, including under your feet. This practice is guaranteed to bring a sense of calm and frees you to stand alone as an individual.

Qigong (chee-guhng) is a Chinese healing art that uses the breath, meditation, and gentle spatial movements to cultivate mastery of one's energy. Qi (chee) refers to the energy within and around us; Gong (guhng) denotes an individual's power to produce an effect. Together, those words signify building the life force in order to balance the mind and body. The practice of Qigong uses simple flowing movements that move energy. They can be fun movements, like those of a monkey, or powerful movements, like those of an eagle. ("Monkey" strengthens the neck and shoulders and imparts the spirited attitude of a monkey. "Eagle" balances physical and emotional energies while instilling the power and beauty of an eagle.) Regardless of the specific movements, Qigong is highly-prized for its ability to dissolve headaches and promote superior health. It's helpful to study Qigong in a class, but you can begin practicing anytime by going on-line and learning from masters who provide simple yet thorough demonstrations.

Experiences with Energy Healing

After my father's funeral, a sea of people filled our backyard patio. I was talking animatedly with a guest while standing across the yard from my brother, Anson. Anson later told me that at one point I waved my hand over my head and the air above me swirled with violet light. This experience was particularly powerful because it happened just days after my father's death.

Even though I had little vocabulary about energies at the time, I knew the violet swirl had something to do with a spiritual connection to love, openness, and the nature of the universe. It took time to assimilate the information I gathered about energy, but that encounter with colored energy opened the door to new possibilities.

Years ago, I attended several spiritually-oriented workshops, each increasing in intensity, duration, and exposure to esoteric practices. Each succeeding workshop increased my understanding and belief in unseen energies. One night during one of these retreats, I sat on the edge of the bed in my hotel room, mesmerized by an exquisite blue and gold light emanating from my hands. I also saw a similar light around a friend's hands. Seeing this colorful energy imbued me with comfort and wonder. I later asked myself why I could see auras at the workshop but not in daily life. I suspect the answer lies in the total immersion and intensity of the week and the proximity of the many high-level metaphysical practitioners that surrounded me. Whatever the cause, that occurrence paved the way for me to recognize invisible and colored energies coming from trees, people—all things.

I was fortunate to experience another form of energy healing when living in Santa Fe. My head hurt so badly at work one day that I thought I was going to faint, except people do not faint from headaches (we just *wish* we could faint). I rose from my desk and gingerly walked to the office of a highly recommended craniosacral therapist who happened to work in the same building. Her name was Claire.

Claire talked with me a moment, then began to treat me. After an hour of lying on her massage table, she encouraged me to free my mind—to let it go back in time. Then, cradling my screaming head in her warm hands, she asked, "Do you see anything?"

I wondered if my visions were real or if I was making them up, but answered her honestly: "A battlefield, a metal helmet, like a conquistador's helmet. An axe in my skull, knives in the base of my head." Claire didn't flinch. She persevered for another hour, using every skill in her repertoire. Overall, this dedicated healer gave me two hours of her exponentially powerful healing energy and time.

As we said goodbye, Claire faced me and held both of my hands, which is when I realized her hands were vibrating like filaments in a bright light bulb. "Your hands are shaking," I said. She told me, "That's the energy." Wow—another pivotal moment in my evolution toward belief in alternative treatments. I wanted more—to understand and to delve into the field of energy medicine.

My awareness of Reiki began when I studied yoga. I asked Linda, my teacher, to show me postures that might release headaches. After proposing relevant asanas, she explained how I could use Reiki to heal myself and gave me the name and phone number of her Reiki Master, Carol. I didn't know what I was getting into but was willing to try anything potentially helpful. Did I have doubts? Yes. Was I skeptical? Oh, yes. But I was also curious and desperate, so despite my uncertainties, I gave Reiki an honest try. When I came away from my first session with sharpened eyesight and a feeling of lightness, calm, and ease, I couldn't wait to return for my next treatment. Every visit with Carol fueled a desire to learn more about Reiki.

Carol used a variety of energy clearing techniques to clear headaches, and after I received my first attunement, she began to teach me how to use Reiki. Reiki training requires attunements. Attunements involve initiations, ceremonies, and specific practices that are a sacred trust. I experienced three levels of attunements from Carol—each one amplifying my overall sense of awareness and the sensitivity of my hands. Over time, the messages I received through subtle variations of energies within my body helped me identify energies in other people.

Today, my midsection talks to me, or my hands tingle when I encounter someone with a headache. Reiki has been a joy and gift of personal discovery for me. It has helped me trust the voice within and provides additional capabilities for helping myself and others with headaches. Reiki is one of my most powerful healing tools.

Pranic Healing sessions have a clearing effect similar to that of Reiki. I've never been trained in Pranic Healing, but I've experienced its power to clear the mental, emotional, and physical states that impede clarity, personal growth, and healing.

One clear, sunny afternoon, my friend, Christina, taught a Qigong class beneath the pecan trees behind my home. We practiced many beneficial movements that day, but the blue sky and a gentle wind created the perfect atmosphere for practicing Eagle. As we moved through the movements of powerful flight, I let myself fall into the experience. The breeze on my outstretched arms felt like wind on feathered, supple wings, and the power of mastering my body like an eagle was stunning. I was surprised at how easily I was able to embody the eagle's majesty, certainty, and strength while also feeling grounded and calm. Eagle is my favorite Qigong practice.

#21

SOUND & MUSIC

When words fail, music speaks.

Shakespeare

Sound is energy traveling through the air, or other mediums, at a specific vibration. Those vibrations affect us in profound and mysterious ways. The whoosh of wind, the cadence of crickets, birdsong, and gurgling mountain streams possess a magical ability to return us to an organic state of rightness that calms, moves, and grounds us. Human-made music can have similar effects and prove invaluable in promoting good health. All forms of positive sound are highly specialized balms that can change body chemistry and release feelings that have camped out in the mind and body.

Medical research shows that those who listen to music are generally happier and less inclined to stress and anxiety (and headaches) than their music-less peers. Numerous studies have proven that music reduces pain and increases productivity and creativity (depending on the type of music— rhythm, tone, and other attributes). In addition to music's intrinsic healing qualities, professional treatments like sound baths, tuning devices, and listening protocols can provide therapeutic assistance.

Sound baths create an atmosphere that generates healing through the use of singing bowls, chimes, and healing harmonies. Tuning devices also create balance in mind and body. One form of sound therapy uses specialized tuning forks that adjust binaural beats. Binaural beats are tones created by the brain to synchronize two different tones played simultaneously—one in each ear. If 210Hz is played in one ear while 200Hz is played in the other, the brain will resonate with the difference in the frequencies—10Hz. Research tells us we can alter our feelings by listening to binaural beats. When someone is in pain (let's say this person has a headache), certain sounds can cancel out the waves that indicate pain.

Other professional sound protocols produce notable positive effects on the autonomic nervous system by providing listening situations that support physiological change. One such intervention was created by Dr. Stephen Porges, Director of the Kinsey Institute Traumatic Stress Research Consortium at Indiana University. Porges' auditory Safe and Sound Protocol (SSP) addresses the chronic states set by trauma that exacerbate physiological problems like headaches, anxiety, and sleep disorders. His SSP treatment uses specialized music to reduce stress and restore the nervous system in a non-intrusive, pleasant way.

In any discussion about sound and music, the value of the human voice deserves a spotlight because the voice expresses feelings. Abject sorrow ranges from silence to weeping. Humor varies from giggles to raucous laughter. Anger appears in grumbles, a tense tone of voice, or shouting. The voice always contains the truth, and what we hear and say, and how we say it, transmits our deepest meanings. If we listen carefully, the messages reflected in our voices can show us how to heal and help us choose healthy behaviors.

Consider what happens when someone directs a tone of derision during a conflict: "Oh, yeah? What are ya gonna do about it?"—the foe becomes more agitated. However, a gentle, loving tone: "Well, I can see I have upset you. I sure didn't mean to," evokes a quiet, non-reactive response.

Researcher Tom Kenyon knows a lot about the power of the voice. His life's mission is healing through song. Kenyon created Acoustic Brain Research, a collective of labs and researchers who delve into the science behind the effects of sound on the brain—psychoacoustics.

In one of Kenyon's studies, he used Brahms lullabies to affect the responses of two sets of preterm babies. One group of babies listened to lullabies; the second group did not. The study revealed that the preterm newborns exposed to Brahms were released from the hospital an average of a week earlier and had fewer health issues than the babies that did not listen to the lullabies. The Brahms babies thrived.

A closer look at the lullaby music Kenyon used in his study reveals a specific structure that soothes the nervous system and increases Alpha brainwave activity, which correlates to lower blood pressure, heart rate, respiration, and stress hormones. A point about the music's architecture: the choice of rhythm, melody, timbre, and high-quality instrumentation are vital components in producing music with the capability to support self-healing.

Additional research used Magnetic Resonance Imaging (MRI) scans to study brain activity while participants listened to music without lyrics. The wordless music lit up the brain's creative (right) side like colorful fireworks. Creativity, of course, leads us to the vanguard of healing—new perspectives.

Although research studies are fascinating, we do not have to be brain scientists to know when a sound heals or hurts us; as you increasingly tune in to the responses of your mind and body, you will instinctively feel the difference.

Experiences with Sound & Music

The nuances of symphonic music were embedded in my family due to my father's love of orchestral music. He played recordings of the world's greatest symphony orchestras almost nightly, and I grew up surrounded by their powerful harmonics. The music of Camille Saint-Saëns', The Swan, so thoroughly resonated with my little girl soul that I almost wore out the grooves on my father's 33LP record. The plaintive notes moved me to dance out the sorrows and beauty they contained. Such experiences were instrumental in teaching me how to express my emotions.

When music touches my sadness, I let myself cry, then I move on. Happy tunes encourage me to bop down grocery store aisles with some swing in my sway. Whenever I'm angry, I hammer out Rachmaninoff on the piano until my anger dissipates. Once the fury is out of my system, I feel calm and instinctively find myself playing soft, delicate melodies.

The sounds of nature always soothe me, so whenever I'm stuck, overly emotional, or confused, I either go to the beach where the sound of ocean waves, seagulls, and wind befriend me, or I visit the forest where the cries of hawks, streams, and rustling leaves fill me with a sense of solidarity and awe. After I am calm, answers to any questions inevitably present themselves.

There is a round house in Montrose, Alabama, with an interior diameter of fourteen feet. The man who built it, Henry Stuart, made each massive concrete block of this one-room jewel by hand. The circular structure and domed ceiling form a space with extraordinary acoustics, and whenever I find myself near Henry's home, I go in, stand in the center of the room, and sing. As my singing ricochets off of the dome, the tones bounce back and through me, literally tuning and balancing my body with my own voice. By the time I get in my car and drive away, my mind is clear, and my body zings with life.

My experience with Safe and Sound's auditory protocol was extremely rewarding. I did the program in conjunction with neurofeedback and benefited notably as my mind and body returned to a more balanced state. My thinking became more clear, and I felt more peaceful. I also felt lighter and was reintroduced to a long-lost friend—easy laughter.

Wind chimes hang on a camellia bush outside my back door. The gentle bong intermittently lowers my stress level, as does an app on my phone: Mind Bell. I set the app to punctuate my day with a gong, and every time it sounds, a sense of peace comes over me—even if I'm in traffic.

My brother, Anson, brought a 45rpm vinyl record to my house one day to share a song he had gone wild about: "The Walk of Life" by Dire Straits. Watching him bounce around to that zippy song embedded such a happy memory in my brain that Anson's dancing image replays like a movie in my mind every time I hear that song. With every review of those moments, the chemistry of joy floods my body even though the originating event happened thirty years ago.

The power of music was also evident after Anson died suddenly (due to complicated medical matters). I had often played the piano for my brother, but I could not bring myself to make music without him. Months later, when I finally pushed my fingers down on the piano keys, deep sorrow poured out in the form of tears and sobs. Music helped me release deep pain. I have learned, on my journey, that emotional expression clears the pathways of my being and waylays headaches. I welcome emotional release. Anytime. Anywhere.

My involvement with sound baths has come in two forms: in groups at spiritual retreats and individually during massages. In group settings, participants relax on yoga mats and pillows while facilitators play singing bowls, chimes, and music. At the end of private massages, singing bowls are used to round out my massage; the vibrations ring through my body and bring each massage to completion on a smooth, graceful note. For me, getting a sound bath is like getting a peace tune-up.

My mother was a sunshine of a woman, full of radiant love—and she sang. She sang while driving the car, poaching eggs for breakfast, trimming camellias, raking the yard, and fixing dinner. Mama just sang. Whenever I played the piano, I could hear her voice singing along from the back of the house. My high school friends regularly asked her to sing The Beatles' song, "Penny Lane." The only words she knew were "Penny Lay-ennn" so she just la-la'd the rest of the tune. My mother's singing not only brought joy, it indirectly taught me to use my voice to express emotion.

22

COLOR

How wonderful the colour yellow is. It stands for the sun.

Vincent Van Gogh

Color is an easy way to support good health because it automatically influences the psyche. Color's power comes from its ability to create calming (anti-headache) atmospheres that affect our moods. Red, for example, increases energy levels—not beneficial when one is angry or has a headache. Soft blue inspires serenity, which is very beneficial for headachy people. When you contemplate the colors in your world, consider the color of your walls, house, car, office, and clothes—and how the color makes you *feel*.

Though individual responses to a specific color may vary, an understanding of the archetypical meanings of basic colors can be instructive:

Yellow: happiness, optimism, vitality, warmth
White: cleanliness, light, purity, innocence, peace
Pink: calmness, romance, nurture, caring

Green: renewal, openness, tranquility, prosperity
Black: power, authority, elegance, formality
Blue: freedom, contemplation, boredom, serenity
Orange: creativity, ambition, cheerfulness
Red: strength, power, vitality, excitement, anger
Brown: authenticity, earthiness, reliability
Purple: luxury, spirituality, mystery, intuition
Grey: heaviness, traditionalism, intelligence

The book, *The Secret Lives of Color,* by Kassia St. Clair, is a treasure trove of fascinating information about color—colors with snazzy names like orpiment and heliotrope. If you read it, keep a stack of sticky notes nearby so you can mark any colors that speak to you, then keep your eyes open for clothes, sheets, shoes, pillows, towels, and such in your chosen colors.

Color is a visible form of light—electromagnetic energy. Each color carries unique healing properties and affects biochemical and hormonal processes that either stimulate or sedate the body's systems and organs. Color is, of course, fundamental to the chakra system.

The chakra system refers to energy centers within the body that correspond to major organs, nerves, and functions. These whirring centers of energy affect our emotional and physical well-being as well as our energetic bodies. There are seven primary chakras that run from the base of the spine (the root chakra) to the top of the head (the crown chakra). Each energy center carries complex characteristics that correspond to a color (red, orange, yellow, green, blue, indigo, violet) that can be used to recalibrate the chakra and return it to maximum function. This is one reason energy healers often direct their clients to imagine inhaling and exhaling various colors of light.

Because humans instinctively sense how color affects them (and their chakras), we only need to tune in and consider which color supports the tasks at hand. It's that simple. If your day calls for heightened intuition, you might be drawn to wear purple. If you don't have purple clothes, accessorize with a violet scarf, or write with a lavender pen. Just find a clever way to incorporate purple into your day.

While we can promote healing through color choices, professional color therapists can help us restore balance to our systems when we need extra support. The practice is called chromotherapy, and many massage therapists and energy medicine practitioners include it in healing sessions. Like acupuncture, chromotherapy is an ancient form of medicine, but it uses color to adjust the body's vibrations to frequencies that support health and harmony.

As you move toward a life free of headaches, you may want to consider how color affects you so you can use it to your advantage. Trust your instincts. If you visit a color therapist, as always, be sure the practitioner is a professional.

Experiences with Color

My family moved from a small apartment into a large, Victorian house when I was five. The twelve-foot ceilings and oak floors were expansive, and I felt like a queen the moment I walked through the front door. French doors and big windows rimmed the main rooms. Light poured through old glass and lay across the wood floors. As my parents walked my brothers and me through the house for the first time, I enjoyed a sense of openness—until my parents showed me my bedroom. My room had only one, albeit large, window, and the walls were a deep shade of blue that felt heavy—downright scary. The color depressed me, but being a polite little girl, I said nothing.

I was twelve when my parents sent my brothers and me to visit our grandmother in South Florida. It was summer, and we spent two happy weeks romping in orange groves and the woods behind Grandmother's house. Upon returning home, we hugged our parents and headed to our respective rooms to unpack our suitcases. As I walked through the door to my room, I froze. My parents had papered my room with rose, cream, and green floral wallpaper and replaced my furniture while we were away. The difference between the dark blue room and the happy *My Fair Lady* room was palpable. I felt brighter; grateful. I wonder how a cheerful decor might have affected my earlier development.

Another significant experience with color came with a house I rented. The interior walls were flesh-colored and I felt like I was living in skin. The landlord was kind enough to let me repaint. I started with the bedroom, graduating the color from sky blue to midnight blue in silhouettes of rolling mountains. Blue tones suited the room's use and induced a state of calm, and the design seamlessly wheeled me from day to night.

The cottage's living room doubled as an office, so I painted three walls parakeet green (the living room), and the fourth wall hibiscus red (the office). The colors suited their purpose, and I felt good every time I entered the house.

As a Reiki student, I followed my teacher's instructions to use various color-related techniques as they related to the chakra system. As I studied each energy center, I wore the color associated with the chakra (red for the base chakra, then up the color scale for each ensuing chakra). The practice refined my understanding of color's archetypical meanings and their relationship to my health and the elements. My clothes also reflect my mood, and as I have grown to be a free and joyful person, I find myself wearing cheerful colors: pink, yellow, blue, coral. If I want to express melancholy feelings, I wear dark colors, but I'm likely to choose pink, orange, or turquoise if I want a lift.

I have always experienced vivid dreams, and during intense healing streaks, visions. One vision featured color as a healing agent for a deep emotional wound I suffered during my teenage years. In the pitch black of deep sleep, the silhouette of a little girl and a grown woman stood in profile looking at each other. The child looked upward into the woman's face; the woman looked downward into the child's face—both child and woman were me. The image was accompanied by a clear message: *Use blue light and hug the little girl.* The moment the woman leaned down to hug the child, there flashed an exquisite blue light—a color I had never seen. I immediately recognized that the message had gifted me with directions for healing my emotional damage. I have held this vision close to my heart and often use the color I saw in the vision for healing purposes.

23

FOOD

Let food be thy medicine.
Thy medicine shall be thy food.

Hippocrates

The body needs nutritious food to replicate healthy cells and fuel bodily processes. As fundamental building blocks of mental and physical health, wholesome foods and wise eating habits are elemental to headache-free living.

To create your world of dietary health, start with consistency. Eat breakfast, lunch, and dinner, and healthy snacks between meals. (Skipping meals is bad headache juju.) Ensure your food is fresh, and exclude processed foods. And because foods have different effects on people, it's essential to observe your physical and mental responses to *specific* foods—sometimes even the healthiest tidbit can trigger a headache.

Lean meats, green, leafy vegetables, and apples are supportive choices, while foods containing tyramine and preservatives belong on a headache not-wanted poster. The Diamond Headache Clinic suggests eating a snack at night, or six small meals spread throughout the day. They also recommend eating fresh foods and avoiding leftovers over two days old (fermented foods are on the do-not-eat list). Wheat has been genetically modified and can cause problematic health issues; stick with non-GMO foods that revitalize the body. Chemical-free fresh foods help stabilize blood vessels, which is one way they keep headaches at bay. (Even though products like glyphosate are proven to be toxic to animals, plants, and people, they continue to be found in many foods, so it's crucial to research your food.)

Food journals can help identify foods that play into your headaches, but if you keep a journal, remember to approach your food-tracking and experimentation with a sense of curiosity; the last thing a headachy person needs is more stress. There is no need to think about food every minute—just be sure to record what you eat, including items like breath mints and cough drops. When you interpret your notes, remember that the effects of eating problematic ingredients may not be evident for a day or two.

MSG (monosodium glutamate), and caffeine are well-known headache culprits. MSG (also labeled "hydrolyzed protein" or "natural flavoring") is often found in foods marketed as health foods. "Healthy" meals often use MSG to keep them from tasting like cardboard. Instead of eating pre-packaged foods, be good to yourself—cook up a pot of fresh, organic broccoli or leeks. Pay attention to subtle changes in how you feel—they are important clues that will help you choose foods that lead to energetic headache-free living.

Many books and online resources list foods to avoid while you are creating a headache-free, healthy body. The book, *The Encyclopedia of Healing Foods* by Michael T. Murray and Joseph E. Pizzorno, suggests eliminating red wine, beer, broad bean pods, pickled anything, sugar, and refined carbs (opt for fruit and vegetables instead of refined carbohydrates). The National Headache Foundation website provides a low-tyramine food program under the *Resources* tab. *The Dizzy Cook* website and cookbook by Alicia Wolf (Alicia had migraines) are fantastic resources for creating good headache-prevention food, including anti-inflammatory smoothies.

It is important to avoid cola, caffeine (coffee, tea, chocolate), aspartame, artificial sweeteners, and foods with nitrates, like bacon, lunch meats, and beef jerky. Most energy bars start out being healthy but become laden with MSG during processing. Aged cheese, nuts, citrus, bananas, and yogurt (it's the tyramine) can also cause headaches. Salt can raise blood pressure and generate headaches, too. Forgo avocados, alcohol, eggs, and dairy. Eliminate canned soups with autolyzed or hydrolyzed yeast.

Instead of ingesting fake foods, go natural and organic. After a few weeks, your body will have cleansed itself. Once you feel good, you can experiment by reintroducing a small amount of a forbidden food item and observe how it affects you. Try eating *half* of a banana, for example, and assess the results. Remember to consider other factors that may affect you, like weather, sleep, travel, and water intake. Try to remove all habits, thoughts, and foods that pour gasoline on the fire of inflammation.

Because inflammation is the enemy of a healthy constitution and a headache-free life, we must count on anti-inflammatory foods to soothe the system and reduce the manufacture of cortisol. A bowl of warm oatmeal with ground flaxseed, cinnamon, almond butter, and local honey is an excellent food combination that delivers the benefit of comfort. (Headache-prone people need all the comfort they can get.) Remember, everything you ingest affects the brain's migrane mechanism.

Minerals help transform food into energy, build strong teeth and bones, and support blood, muscle, skin, hair, and nerve function. Potassium maintains proper fluid balance and muscle. Calcium not only builds healthy bone but helps regulate blood pressure.

Fresh fruits and vegetables are excellent sources of minerals. One orange delivers a daily dose of vitamin A in whole-food form. It also provides a health-friendly dose of fiber and phytochemicals that ward off diabetes, osteoporosis, cancer, and heart disease. That said, too much vitamin A can improve symptoms but result in inflammation. So once again, we must listen to the nuances of our bodies.

We haven't talked about medicines yet, but we will. For now, let's just say it's hard to read the clues that reveal food triggers if the body is numb from prescription medications. Pain medicines don't only target the head—they fill the entire body, making it impossible to feel changes in physiology—something to think about.

When modifying food choices, it's helpful to remain calm. I once gained fifteen pounds, and the more I worried about it, the harder it was to shed the extra weight. I ate salad with lemon juice dressing and grapefruit for an entire month. Then I ate half a cheesecake. Deprivation is a no-no. A balanced selection of natural foods is a yes-yes.

To move toward good physical health, it's a good idea to eliminate the word "diet"—it has the word "die" in it. Nobody wants to die. And let go of the word "lose," as in "lose weight," or "losing weight," or "lost weight." Nobody wants to lose anything, either. Think of healthy eating as gaining good health and joyful living. The difference in perspective and how we talk to ourselves can be crucial.

While we cannot alter headache triggers like weather, we can choose habits and foods that support a healthy body, and a healthy life—a life free of headaches.

Experiences with Food

Despite my massage therapist friends repeatedly telling me that "sugar is poison," I occasionally eat a small slice of homemade cherry pie or drink half of a cola. The resulting headache is quick to announce my folly. I am always sorry when this happens. I can get away with eating pie or drinking a sip of cola when no other headache triggers are afoot, but because such occasions are rare, I usually eat pure foods and drink healthy beverages. My drink of choice, for example, has become pomegranate juice diluted in filtered water. It is a beautiful color, tastes good, and promotes good health.

Now that I am older and my hormones no longer run me up and down a flagpole (and my migraine threshold is spacious), I can occasionally eat a brownie or a little cheese and still sidestep a headache. But normally, eating forbidden foods is not worth the risk of pain—or lethargy, for that matter. During the years my hormones ran full bore, I worked like a lunatic, ate *everything*, and was a stressed perfectionist. I lived with a headache that rose to agonizing proportions at the slightest provocation—if you can call that living. Eliminating food triggers would have helped me, but at the time I didn't know how food affected headaches; neither did I want to educate myself or bother to track my food intake. I certainly didn't want to give up coffee.

Until I developed healthy eating habits, the subtle effects of detrimental foods were masked by caffeine and other inflammatory foodstuffs—not-to-mention prescription pain-killers. I didn't notice *anything* about food triggers until my body was free of pain medicine. After I eliminated drugs and cleaned up my eating act, I realized how processed foods sapped my energy and served up a big plate of headache. (If I eat processed yogurt, for example, I feel lousy immediately— then a headache slides in.) In general, I feel best when I eat less food because eating less reduces my exposure to food-related headache triggers.

Salt is not my friend, either. My ears have been ringing ever since a sound system blasted my eardrums. If I eat pizza or spaghetti with red sauce, the volume of the tinnitus doubles within half an hour. It's the salt, and the negative effects of salt on blood pressure (therefore headaches), are well-documented.

As I pay attention to the subtle physiological changes food causes, it becomes easier to make choices that support my life. Eating clean food provides me with limitless energy, a clear mind, and loose-fitting jeans. It allows me to thrive.

This handy list of food triggers makes it easy to eliminate items that initiate headaches:

CAFFEINE	Coffee, tea, & cola. Even decaf coffee and tea (they contain additional chemical triggers). Also, beware of coffee substitutes. Try caffeine-free herb tea (without trigger flavors like citrus).
CHOCOLATE	White chocolate (no cocoa) is okay; carob is questionable.
MONOSODIAM GLUTAMATE (MSG)	Chinese and other restaurant food; soups and bouillons; Accent and seasoned salt; flavored, salty snacks; croutons and bread crumbs; gravies; ready-to-eat meals; cheap buffets; processed meats; veggie burgers; protein concentrates; and low-fat, low-calorie foods.
PROCESSED MEAT AND FISH	Aged, canned, cured, fermented, marinated, smoked, tenderized—or preserved with nitrites or nitrates. Hot dogs, sausage, salami, pepperoni, bologna (and other lunchmeats with nitrites), liverwurst, beef jerky, certain hams, bacon, pâtés, smoked or pickled fish, caviar, and anchovies. Also, fresh beef liver and chicken livers, and wild game (contains tyramine).
CHEESE AND OTHER DAIRY PRODUCTS	The more aged, the worse. Permissible cheeses include cottage cheese, ricotta, cream cheese, and good-quality American cheese. Beware of cheese-containing foods, including pizza, yogurt (including frozen yogurt), sour cream, and buttermilk.
ALCOHOL & VINEGAR	Especially red wine, champagne, and dark or heavy drinks. Vodka is best tolerated. Clear (ideally, distilled) vinegar is allowable. Don't overdo condiments made with vinegar (ketchup, mustard, and mayonnaise).

NUTS	Avoid all nuts and nut butters. Seeds are okay.
CERTAIN FRUITS & JUICES	Citrus fruits (oranges, grapefruit, lemons, limes tangerines, clementines, pineapple) and their juices, as well as bananas. Also avoid raisins and other dried fruits if preserved with sulfites, raspberries, red plums, papayas, passion fruit, figs, dates, and avocados.
CERTAIN VEGETABLES, ESPECIALLY ONIONS	Sauerkraut, pea pods, and certain beans: broad Italian, lima, fava, navy beans, and lentils. Allowed: leeks, scallions, shallots, spring onions, and garlic.
FRESH YEAST-RISEN BAKED GOODS	Less than one day old homemade or restaurant-baked breads, especially sourdough, as well as bagels, doughnuts, pizza dough, soft pretzels, and coffee cake.
ASPARTAME (NUTRASWEET)	Saccharin (Sweet'n Low) may also be a trigger for some. Splenda may not be a problem.
OTHERS	Perhaps soy products, especially if cultured (miso), fermented (tempeh), or otherwise highly processed (e.g., soy protein isolate/concentrate). Watch out for soy sauce containing MSG. Less risky are unflavored tofu and soy milk and flour. Soy oil is safe. Possibly tomatoes and tomato-based sauces, mushrooms, and whatever gives you a headache.

From *Heal Your Headache: The 1-2-3 Program for Taking Charge of Your Pain* (2002) by David Buchholz, MD

24

MOON,
WEATHER & ALTITUDE

There is a moon inside every human being.
Learn to be companions with it.

Rumi

It is mesmerizing to watch a full moon lift her pretty face over the edge of a darkened mountain range or lay melted light onto the surface of a lake. But that same beautiful moon can have a devastating effect on people with headaches. So can low barometric pressure, humidity, ozone, and high altitudes. We may have no control over these elements, but we can free ourselves from being their hostages.

How? By adjusting our lives around full moons, low-pressure systems, and altitude changes. If I ever make it to Machu Picchu, I will plan my trip when there is no full moon, and I will rest at lower elevations before I ascend to higher atmospheres. I would also avoid planning my honeymoon during the most stressful phase of my menstrual cycle, and leave plenty of blank, easy-going space on my calendar.

The effects of high altitude result from reduced atmospheric pressure and decreased oxygen levels. Any *quick* ascension makes matters worse because the body needs time to acclimate. Mountain climbers and athletes who travel to high mountain areas for competitions arrive early to give their bodies time to adapt to the thinner atmosphere—so must we.

While some altitude-related symptoms signal severe problems (and should be taken seriously), most altitude sickness is harmless. "Acute Mountain Sickness," for example, exhibits symptoms like nausea, dizziness, and headaches, but is the least dangerous of the altitude illnesses. Mountain sickness can be avoided by ascending gradually and taking time to rest. The symptoms decrease when one returns to lower altitudes—the quicker the descent, the better.

Weather systems bring changes in barometric pressure that can also play havoc with the headache-prone. Scientists believe that weather affects headaches because it changes brain chemistry (like serotonin levels). The solution is to correct as many other factors as possible. This approach keeps the weather from ganging up with other existing triggers and starting a headache riot.

Studies link the moon with circadian rhythms, hormonal fluctuations, sleep patterns, and the moon's pull on the tides and our bodies. There's no excess of research on the subject, probably because it would take the focus of a field mouse to figure out all of the connections, but anyone with headaches can attest to the veracity of the effects of the moon.

Our best defense to changes in weather, altitude, and the moon is our best offense: organize your life so it is as balanced and as healthy as you can make it. Back away from the type-A routine. Schedule a manicure, pedicure, or massage to offset the effects of these powerful forces of nature. Take a day off. Take two. Stay on a routine. Get your sleep. Relax your work-out intensity. Lessen your salt intake. Let go of guilt. Paint a picture. Distract yourself with novel experiences.

It's easy to forget about the influence of elements like the moon, weather, and altitude when you feel good, but to live headache-free, it's necessary to pay attention to them so you can make adjustments before they affect you.

Experiences with the Moon, Weather & Altitude

During the worst of my headache years, the full moon was a harbinger of hell. Just *seeing* a full moon launched a massive headache.

After years of fearing full moons, I found myself hiking in Arches National Park in the Utah desert. As I wandered up the slow grade to the park's landmark arch, the beauty of nature's terracotta sculptures and blue sky took me so far outside my familiar world that I stopped thinking.

As evening eased into night, I stared wide-eyed as a massive full moon rose over the red earth. I was completely grounded in the moment; things just felt right. Then it struck me—*I was looking at a bright, full moon and didn't have a headache!* It was the first time in twenty-one years. As I stood there, years of braced emotions washed my face with tears.

With the elimination of stress, I had become free. No person and no cultural mores were pressing on me; neither did I have responsibilities of work or self-imposed pressure. I had also stopped excessively exercising my body. I was quiet—present with my surroundings. Fully alive.

When I re-entered the world of work and requirements, I had to find a way to maintain the same balance and peace.

Little by little, I realized it was possible to live free from headaches and enjoy life, including full moons.

The effects of altitude became apparent through a variety of experiences, but the most notable occurred during a road trip from Texas to Colorado. By the time I reached the infamous Raton Pass in New Mexico, I had changed elevation by seven thousand feet in one day. My head was screaming. I finally stopped the car, ate pasta, then continued up and over the mountain pass. As soon as I began to descend the mountain, the headache began to diminish. The experience was another lesson in the operations of headaches.

I once tried to hike the Keyhole in Colorado and had to turn back within twenty minutes because the altitude, exertion, and possibly inadequate hydration, initiated a killer headache. I went home, made a cup of chamomile tea, and put an ice pack on my head. Now that I know how to avoid headaches, I may give the Keyhole another try.

Low-pressure systems used to steamroll me with headaches because instead of easing up when I sensed a storm, I kept my foot on life's accelerator and ploughed forward full throttle—then I would take pain killers. Things got better when I started taking care of myself. I did my emotional healing work, dedicated myself to healthy habits, and lightened up. For me, the only solution to outside forces like weather and altitude is to go into stealth mode—get extra quiet, extra relaxed, and maintain wholesome practices.

#25

MEDICINES &
DOCTORS

Drugs are delusive; they do not adjust anything.

D. D. Palmer

Medicine can play a valuable role in eliminating chronic headaches because it buys time away from pain, but it is not a true or permanent solution. Pain is not the causal problem. Pain is a symptom. Headache medicine is appropriate for providing temporary relief while we install healthy, long-term solutions into our lives. Because pain medicines mask causes and keep the pain cycle going, it's imperative to replace them with healthy practices as swiftly as possible.

After experiencing headaches for an extended time, one can develop the *habit* of having headaches, in which case even a small headache can cause so much stress it builds into monstrous head pain. It's the fear. Once a person has been run over by a train, they get understandably nervous when the tracks start to rumble or a whistle blows in the distance. That's why the warning bells of a headache often result in a trip to the medicine cabinet. Even the *word* "headache" can have a negative impact. The cycle of pain-equals-medicine can be upended, however, by a collection of healthy choices that leave room for a pain-free body and mind. After you have installed your health-producing assortment of new habits, you probably will not need medicines. Until you have created your unique restorative path, however, it is crucial to arm yourself with knowledge and locate a physician who complements your needs. Too many Western medical doctors prescribe drugs because they don't know what else to do. To be fair, a medical doctor trained in Western medicine has little time to study holistic and alternative practices. Brief office visits don't give physicians enough time to consider the many details that affect an individual's health. Sometimes they simply do not understand the new treatment protocols. That's why we have to be our own Sherlock Holmes and find the clues in our everyday lives that allow us to advocate for ourselves and solve the headache mystery.

The clues are also valuable guides for your physician— if you have a holistic doctor who *listens* to you. Because painkillers numb the entire body, not just the head, they block the very systems designed to alert us to trouble. If the body and mind are numb and disconnected, it's impossible to pick up on the messages your masterful physiology is trying to deliver. This is an agonizing truth that *you* must manage— and it is a truth rarely discussed in a medical office. How can we find answers if we can't sense the changes in our bodies? We can't. This means the diagnosis will *never* be correct, much less the solution. I repeat—I *never* noticed how yogurt triggered my headaches until my body had been un-numbed (I'd take pain pills and *eat more yogurt!*), and there were many other triggers I hadn't noticed. I weep to consider the hells I could have avoided had I realized what painkillers were doing to me. One of the most direct messages I will deliver in this volume is to regard painkillers with extreme caution; they are threats to health.

There are numerous reasons why vessels swell in the brain, and those reasons form a collective: unresolved emotional issues (guilt, shame, fear, anger), technology overload, inflammatory foods, sleeplessness, high altitude, hormonal fluctuations, barometric pressure changes, stress, and other factors. When we overload our systems, we surpass our tolerance level, and that's when we hear the warning: *Too much! Stop!* That voice will eventually *scream* at us: *TOO MUCH! STOP ALREADY!* and it will increase the pain level (and other symptoms) until it is heeded. Sadly, some people learn to live in pain; it becomes their normal state of being. Then, instead of solving the causal problems, they live life through the lens of headaches or other maladies.

Many medications are formulated to constrict the swollen vessels associated with headaches. The constriction reduces pain, but as soon as the medicine wears off, the vessels swell, becoming larger than their original state. *Yowza!* Then, most people take *more* medicine so they can press onward, grateful for the temporary relief medication brings. Of course, they are grateful! But, such choices result in rebound headaches and create an endless cycle of head pain.

I refer you again to the book, *Heal Your Headache*, in which David Buchholz, MD, Neurology, Johns Hopkins Medicine, discusses how certain chemicals push our thresholds down and make us more susceptible to triggers. He also shares ways to eliminate vessel-constricting medications and substances, including, forgive me, coffee. Even decaf.

Caffeine is a drug. The rule is "zero caffeine," and that includes colas, chocolate, and high-powered energy drinks. Because coffee constricts vessels, it initially brings headache relief, so it's tempting to think of it as a harmless solution, but there's still that darn rebound business. So call on your courage and your desire to thrive and just do it—eliminate caffeine.

Drugs can make us victims. They can cause us to rely on doctors and medicine to treat our problems instead of doing our part to solve them at the root level. Preventive methods cannot work if medicinal rebound is running the show. The failure is never due to wholesome remedies; it's the result of drugs and bad habits that yank us all over the place. Healthy choices are our hope and lead to freedom from pain.

Humans can bear a certain amount of stress: physical stress, environmental stress, and emotional stress. When we exceed our limit, the result is a malady—like ulcers or headaches. The goal is to leave ourselves some breathing room and eliminate triggers. Headache triggers come in two forms—those we cannot control and those we can. They include:

Perfume
Cleaning supplies and chemicals
Paint fumes
Hormonal fluctuations
Technology overload

Noise
Certain foods
Skipping meals
Certain medicines
Lack of sleep
Too much sleep
Bright or flickering light
Changes in daylight hours
Lack of consistency of schedule
Emotional build-up
Speed of life
Barometric pressure
Altitude changes
Depression (including from pain or headaches)
Lack of exercise
Over-exercise
Sex
No sex
Diet pills
Birth control pills
Protein drinks
Certain hormone replacement therapies
Long-term use of decongestants
Whatever is specific to you

It's easy to identify which items on this list are within our control and which are not. Some of them may not affect you, but they might affect me. Irrespective of any ambiguity, it is beneficial to replace harmful habits with supportive practices.

Prescription for Nutritional Healing by Phyllis A. Balch, CNC, is a reference book of natural supplements for healing.

The book includes an easy-to-read section of fascinating information about nutrition and detailed solutions for a multitude of disorders. The headache portion provides preventative remedies like chelated calcium, which alleviates muscular tension, and cayenne, which thins the blood and increases circulation. The book contains a list of solutions, complete with dosages and contraindications. It's a handy resource guide that may provide you with options if you decide to wean yourself off of prescription medicines. Use common sense when applying the information to your situation. Make changes slowly. Talk to your nutritionist and physician if you have questions.

Eliminating prescription headache drugs requires an intentional, daily focus on happiness and the strength to make healthy choices. It also requires addressing emotional wounds and psychological damage. If you need doctors and medications while you create a healthful foundation, choose them wisely. Remember: pain is the *result* of a problem. Solutions are found in identifying and clearing up causes.

Experiences with Medicines & Doctors

My first neurologist prescribed various preventative medications like Inderal, and when they didn't work, he moved me into painkillers like Fiorinal and Fiorinal #3, which contains codeine. Sure enough, the vessels in my head would swell, then constrict, then swell with a vengeance. At the time, I was unaware of the rebound phenomenon and took Fiorinal with codeine for seven years. My stay at the Diamond

Headache Clinic in Chicago started me on the road to finding alternative solutions and eliminating rebound medications, but eventually, I had to go home. With my top-notch doctors being geographically far away and my fledgling knowledge about headaches, it wasn't long before a local neurologist prescribed painkillers to me again. He lacked awareness of alternative solutions. (When I mentioned yoga to him, he dismissed the idea: "It won't hurt anything.") Unfortunately, there was never a scarcity of doctors who would prescribe painkillers.

If an observant practitioner or doctor had studied my crooked back, ordered X-rays, and asked about my lifestyle and emotional wounds, answers would have revealed themselves sooner. But not one physician asked me in-depth questions, and because I was an intense nut to crack, my path to freedom was long and winding. Solutions to my pain unfolded one petal at a time, and that is how I found the clues to eliminating headaches—slowly. Undoubtedly, there were times when medicine made my life bearable, but it also dulled my emotions—the very feelings that would have promoted healing. It was impossible to think clearly or accurately process my emotions while taking drugs or being in pain. It seemed an unsolvable dilemma. One physician charmed me when she said, "You know, we doctors don't know what to do for people with headaches." I appreciated her honesty and the confirmation of my suspicions.

During the years I took Fiorinal with codeine, not once did I research the medication. You know what's in it? Aspirin (thinned my blood), caffeine (inflamed my vessels and caused rebound headaches), and butalbital (addictive). The effects of this drug were pointed out to me when my friend, Eileen, and I went to lunch one day. I felt a headache coming on (stress and rebound headache), so I took the Fiorinal. Ten minutes into our meal, the medication kicked in, bringing a familiar, unfortunate edginess with it. Eileen commented, "Wow. That medication really changes your personality." I felt embarrassed and ashamed. Later, when I was alone, I recognized the accuracy of her observation. The realization spurred me forward in my search for answers.

I also took Imitrex for years. First, the tablets. Then the nasal spray. Then injections—self-injected. Imitrex seemed to save me. I am grateful for this drug and the ability of similar medicines to tamp down a headache, but in a sense, I wasn't really living. I was *trying* to live—with headaches. Imitrex is a triptan, and unbeknownst to me, it was keeping me in an endless headache loop. Eventually, it exhausted me within thirty minutes. I quit taking it.

The impact of medicine in my life showed itself in a formal photograph of my family. On the morning we sat for the photographer, I had my usual headache, so I took medication in an effort to feel normal. When I reviewed the proofs, all I could see was the headache lurking behind my vague, unfocused eyes. That image reflected the truth and triggered powerful feelings of sorrow, shame, and guilt. I realized I lived in a public state of perpetual tension, pretending to be okay, waiting for the next headache to hit me.

On another occasion, Lou, my husband at the time, was driving me home after a visit to the ER, where I had been given a shot for pain and an injection of Phenergan (promethazine). We were nearing our house when my heart revved to the rhythm of a hummingbird's wings. "Lou," I said. "We need to go back. Fast."

He drove fast.

My heart was beating so frantically it was unimaginable it could keep going. "We need to get there . . ."

He drove faster.

As the heavy car swung up to the ER, I flipped open the door handle, and half fell out of the car into the arms of three attendants who had rushed out when they saw us roar in. I was in a wheelchair before my second foot touched the ground. The Phenergan had affected my heart rate. The experience was truly frightening and shook my faith in medicine.

In regard to the headache hell I lived in, for years I thought, *I just need to stop taking medicine, go into the desert and lie on the ground and wait. Do some kind of Vision Quest. I need to purify myself. The headaches will be horrible, but then I'll be okay. I should get it over with.* But I did not get it over with. I wasn't ready. So I ignored the real problems, effectively extending my time in headache jail for years.

Eventually, coffee replaced prescription drugs. At the first hint of a headache, I would find the nearest Starbuck's and indulge in a grande latte, two vanilla bean scones, and an Advil or two. I thanked God for coffee until I realized that coffee was causing extensive muscle tension *and* rebound headaches. When I stopped drinking coffee, my entire body relaxed. I had a headache for two days while my system adjusted, but afterward, life improved dramatically.

During a conversation about headaches I asked one doctor, "What do you think causes headaches?"

He answered: "Doctors have about three minutes to talk to a patient before they prescribe drugs. There's no good diagnosis. Do you know that forty-two percent of the American population is taking some kind of pain medication—narcotics, pain relief—illegal or legal?"

"Where did you find that statistic?"

"At last year's medical conference." (The year was 2018.)

The more I learn, the more I trust myself to be my best advocate.

Now that the worst headache phase of my life is over, I can look back at the road I traveled, including the times when the smokescreen of medicine helped me live my life. But I could have shortened that painful portion of my journey had I been able to let go of my preconceived notions, my perceived unforgivable errors, the tension from emotional trauma, prescription drugs, and foods that triggered headaches. Had I just stopped running and pushing, I would have been forced to lay low sooner. Medicine simultaneously helped and prolonged my agony.

Eventually, I participated in sweat lodges, journeys to the West, workshops with names like *Independency, Magic Maker,* and *Dream Quest.* I went to priests for absolution of any harm I had ever caused and visited St. Peter's Cathedral in Rome. I stayed in monasteries where I practiced silence. I tested my spirituality. There were mountains I climbed and deserted roads I traveled alone. I paid attention, tried new things, and kept learning. I kept healing.

Turns out, I was on the right track with that Vision Quest idea, but I did it at the pace of a dawdling snail.

26

HORMONES

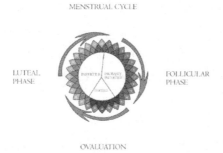

hor·mone\ 'hór-mōn\n [Gr hormōn, prp. Of horman to stir up
1 : a product of living cells that circulates in body fluids
(such as blood) or sap and produces a specific
often stimulatory effect on the activity of cells
usually remote from its point of origin

Webster's Dictionary

Hormones are crucial to the intricate operations of the human body and mind. They operate processes like blood pressure, sexual desire, and hunger, and they do it as dependably as the orbit of the moon. Despite their remarkable function, however, hormonal cycles can be troublesome for the headache-prone woman. We are specifically talking about the ups and downs of progesterone, testosterone, and the T-Rex of female hormones—estrogen. Every month of the menstruating woman's life, this trio does a carefully orchestrated dance in her fertile fields, imparting pressure on the psyche and the body. Moontime, as indigenous people call it, is the ideal time to go on a retreat—even if it's a small, homemade mini-retreat. Meditate. Go for gentle walks in nature. Reduce life's intensity level. Find a way to tame your menstrual tiger.

A journal or chart can help identify the phases of your personal cycle and reveal how your psycho-emotional and physical states align with your monthly rhythms. If you decide to keep a journal, be sure to include *where* headaches fall on your cyclical timeline. After three months, your chart may reveal a pattern that indicates where to make peace-producing changes that can soften the most stressful phase. Perhaps you will benefit from turning off your cell phone, changing your diet, or getting a massage. Opt for anything that lets you lie down on the tiger's back and breathe for a while.

Because significantly more women have headaches than men, most research studies focus on females. There are, however, some small studies on males. These studies correlate elevated estrogen levels with lower levels of testosterone in non-obese men. The key is in the ratio of estrogen to testosterone. More research is needed, but several studies have implicated estrogen in the development, frequency, and severity of migraines in men. Regardless of gender, hormones impact our health.

As you analyze your health and hormones, remember that plastic containers leach estrogen-like chemicals into foods and liquids. These chemicals are toxic and affect estrogen levels. Avoid foods wrapped in plastic and use a recyclable glass or metal water bottle. Everything we breathe, drink, touch, think, and eat affects our physiology and health.

The forces that drive body chemistry are powerful, so we must attune ourselves to the intricate mechanisms that are a part of our very being. We may not be able to change our cycles, but we can counterbalance their effects by making wise choices.

Experiences with Hormones

Starting at age fifteen, my hormones played a starring role in a once-monthly personal performance of *The Menstrual Beast*. Even though my nature was intrinsically kind and polite, I felt explosive when the pressure exerted by hormones contracted their way into my life every twenty-eight days. There are things ladies do not say or do in the South, but for one week every month, volumes of stacked emotions roared out of me in wild, frustrated form. I was already a sensitive person, and menstrual hormones amped up that sensitivity until I was a human cannon packed with an overload of emotional gunpowder.

The first time I monkeyed with my hormones, my entire system went haywire: birth control pills. I was bloated, developed saddlebag hips, and my personality changed. I was miserable. I took the pill just long enough to permanently install the saddlebags. I tried an IUD once, but it was laced with hormones that made me crazy, and then the thing got lost inside my body. After that, I said no thank you to altering my body's natural state.

After I understood hormones and the other factors underlying headaches, I left plenty of open space around the most pressurized phase of my menstrual cycle. Eventually, menopause-related hormonal changes proved invaluable in reducing and ultimately eliminating my headaches.

#21

STRUCTURAL ELEMENTS

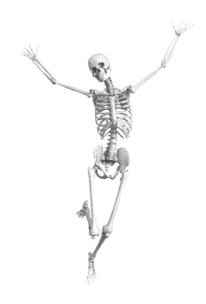

One would think it would be most unwise in a man
to be afraid of a skeleton, since Nature has set curious
and quite insuperable obstacles to his running away from it.

G. K. Chesterton, *The Defendant*

The structural components of our remarkable bodies can play a fundamental role in causing or exacerbating headaches. Because the body is a coordinated mechanism ("the hip bone connected to the—thigh bone, the thigh bone connected to the—shin bone . . ."), the connectivity of the parts is a topic worth examination. Alignment is of paramount importance. The head should be balanced over the shoulders, the shoulders over the hips, the hips over the feet. An off-kilter structure causes trouble. It can cause headaches. Take the jaw, for instance.

During an office exam, my dentist and I got into a conversation about headaches and jaws. Since my mouth was propped open, he did most of the talking.

"Yes," he said. "Stress and jaws are definitely related to headaches. I just treated two eight-year-old children who were having major headaches because their jaws were jammed from gritting their teeth."

I said, "*Whaaa!?*"

Clenched jaws are buddies with headaches because excess mandibular tension causes a whole collection of muscles to revolt. These muscular rebels include the trapeziuses (shoulders), sternocleidomastoids (large muscles connecting collar bones to the side/back of the head), the masseters (muscles joining upper cheek to lower jaw), and other muscles and tendons. Extreme stress causes these components to react; muscles contract, bones misalign, and tooth-grinding ensues, along with headaches.

Fortunately, the symptoms can be alleviated with therapy, customized mouthguards, and the reduction of stress. The guidepost for jaw-clenching is: your teeth shouldn't touch unless you are chewing food. If your teeth touch when you aren't eating, you may want to evaluate the source of your stress and ask a capable dentist to analyze your bite and supply you with a mouthguard.

Tight jaws, of course, are just one example of how misalignment can hurt the headache-prone. An out-of-place rib or vertebrae causes the body to compensate by reassigning workload and placing excessive demands on inappropriate muscle groups. A tweak caused by sleeping in an awkward position can result in sciatica. Leaning toward a computer screen for hours can wreak structural mayhem. If you work on a computer, you might check the position of your monitor. Be sure your head is comfortably balanced over your torso, elbows by your sides, shoulders back and down. Let your skeleton stack itself. Invest in an adjustable office chair. Take regular breaks. Rest your eyes. Get up, walk around, and stretch. These are healthy habits, with or without headaches.

When there is reason to believe a structural element is negatively affecting the body, it's wise to gather the appropriate medical information through analysis and logic. Investigate. Tests like X-rays can reveal structural anomalies and point to solutions that lead to headache-free living. Also, remember the role of muscle in maintaining stability and proper motor function. Your alignment may benefit from strengthening specific muscle groups. If you need instruction about proper alignment and muscle training, you will likely benefit from having a professional design an exercise program for you.

Experiences with Structural Elements

I was eight years of age when my parents questioned the inward turn of my right leg. They took me to a physician who provided two options for correction: leg braces or clunky brown orthopedic brogans. My parents chose the shoes: U-G-L-Y. I wore them twice before tossing them to the back of the closet. Zoom forward forty-five years to the day my chiropractor pointed to an X-ray that revealed an extra piece of bone suspended in the space between my lower spine and its neighboring pelvic flare (iliac crest). That little bone caused my leg to turn in, my back to curve, my hips to swerve, and my right shoulder to rise. It also explained the range of movement problems I had encountered in athletic endeavors.

When the chiropractor showed me the X-rays of that piece of bone, the torqued and tilted pelvis, and my crooked spine, a profound sorrow filled me—the kind of sadness you might feel when discovering your child has a problem. I wondered why previous doctors had not delved into the reasons for my crooked body and pondered the horrors I would have endured had my doctor put me in *leg braces* at age eight. The experience made me more aware of the need to be my own intuitive health detective and persuaded me to stop doing back-flips or pushing myself in yoga poses that hurt. It also convinced me that I needed to customize my exercise and stretching methods.

Structural problems were especially pronounced during my dancing days. One night, I was at the barre practicing arabesques when I observed my dance teacher, Major, and the owner of the dance school, Elvie, conversing and glancing my way. Soon enough, they walked over for a closer look at my form. They watched for a moment, tilted their heads like cocker spaniels, and then Major announced, "I think it's her *ribs.*" He then requested I pull them inward. Well, when I pulled my ribs in, my head poked forward, my hips tucked under, and my knees bent. Nice look for a ballerina.

Likewise, during my karate days, my right leg effortlessly moved forward and up, allowing me to deliver a very spiffy front kick, but it refused to go backwards with the same ease—that extra piece of bone was in the way. Of course, I didn't know it even existed at the time. I'm convinced that X-rays would have revealed the reason for my limited range of motion. The information wouldn't have improved my form, but it might have helped me modify my workouts and diminish the headaches.

I have broken my nose three times through interactions with a baseball, a karate punch, and a dog's head. One doctor thought my broken nose might be causing headaches due to a reduction in oxygen intake. He tested his theory by administering pure oxygen. Oxygen was not the answer. An ear, nose, and throat (ENT) doctor thought the alignment of the broken nose might be causing the headaches, so he inserted four eight-inch-long codeine-laced needles into the back of my nose—through my nose. Imagine the fun. The result? No. The broken nose wasn't the problem. (What we headache people go through.)

Tension and pain frequently caused me to clench my jaws and teeth during my sleep until my dentist made a custom mouthguard for me. The mouthguard was invaluable in relieving jaw tension, protecting my teeth, and dismantling headaches. I still sleep in the same device because even though it bears marks from the days I was so anxious I bit holes through the plastic, it continues to relax my jaw muscles and keeps my teeth in alignment.

One of my favorite activities is participating in Zumba classes. When I first began Zumba, I attended two classes a week, then gradually added a third. After a year, my core strength and alignment had notably improved. As my body became strong and properly aligned, my headaches retreated.

SUBTLE MATTERS

INTRODUCTION TO SUBTLE MATTERS

Now that we have discussed concrete topics relating to headache release, we are ready to address matters with squiggly edges. In short, we are entering the world of intangibles—the woo-woo.

I hope you snuggle up with a warm cup of herbal tea and read this section with a sense of curiosity. Some readers may think these chapters are "really out there" while others will consider the topics to be child's play in the arena of cosmic possibilities.

Have fun as you sift through these esoteric chapters. Check any previous conceptions at the door. If a topic seems odd to you, keep peering at it for a while—you may realize it's useful in unexpected ways. And let me say the obvious: I am me, and you are you. Your trajectory to healing will differ from mine. But even though the surface details of our lives vary, at the core, we are made of the same stuff. So, as you walk through this hall of possibilities, don't be afraid to open the closets—the closets where no one else has looked. You may (or may not) find something relevant there.

All of the stories are true and, for me, are at the heart of letting go of headaches.

28

VISUALIZATION & BIOFEEDBACK

Imagination is the beginning of creation.
You imagine what you desire, you will what you imagine,
and at last you create what you will.

George Bernard Shaw

For two weeks in the late 1980's I was a patient at the Diamond Headache Clinic, where I learned new approaches to recreating a life without headaches. First, my doctor replaced my hardcore pain medication with a mild, orange concoction. While my system was recalibrating, the medical staff watched over me—gave me shots when the pain was out of control and introduced me to art therapy, healthy food habits, relaxation techniques, headache-related classes, and a psychologist. I was wound so tightly that my treatment included massage. One massage, in particular, delivered a mind-bending experience that showed me how easily a headache could vanish.

On the memorable day, I lay on the massage therapist's table, hoping to God the man could take away the relentless pain in my head and the knotted, steel-like muscles in my neck and shoulders. Before we began, he placed headphones over my ears. *Hmm, I thought. This is something new.* The first thing I heard was a Sean Connery-like voice, rich like heirloom gold, with a soft English accent. I drifted away as the voice led me step-by-step into a scene painted by mesmerizing intonations: *You are walking on a warm, sandy beach . . . you are feeling so relaxed. You feel your feet on the soft, warm sand, a breeze on your skin . . .* As the massage proceeded, I gave my body to the therapist and my mind to the soothing voice: *You are so relaxed. You are relaxing more and more. You feel sooo good.* For all practical purposes, Elizabeth Phelps was walking barefoot on a warm, sandy beach. I *felt* the sand on my feet and *heard* the waves rolling in—the seagulls calling. The voice continued to lead me along the shore to a treasure chest half-buried in the sand. I opened it . . .

When the massage was over, and the recording ended, I sat up—astonished. For the first time in years, I was as relaxed as a trusting two-year-old. *No sign* of tension or a headache. Zero pain. My physiology had entirely changed. Of course, the massage was essential to the positive outcome, but I have had hundreds of massages—none of them restored my absolute peace like *this* one. The mental journey gets credit for turning off the headache switch.

An identical response to mind movies can be seen in cats and dogs when they dream they are being chased—all twitching paws and legs running as they sleep. Dreaming humans operate the same way—jerking to catch themselves when they stumble in the dream world. The body responds to the mind's perceptions, and it doesn't matter if experiences are real or imagined—if we are awake or asleep. Listening to the recording at the Diamond Headache Clinic and visualizing a peaceful experience modified my mind and my body chemistry. It wasn't magic, but it *felt* like magic. A massage, an hour of changing my mental story, and *Voilà!*—I was well.

A darker example involved dreaming an intruder was in my house. I was asleep in the dream, but I could see the prowler. She slid open my glass door then silently moved around my room, checking out my things—my desk, my open notebook, my sofa pillows. And there I was in bed, eyes closed, observing her as she slithered around my house like a creepy-crawly. She finally made her way to the side of my bed and stood there staring at me (the sleeping me). I tried to scream, but I was so terrified I couldn't make a sound. My wild heartbeat and terror awakened me. Just *writing* about that dream pumps adrenaline into my body.

Research is revealing more about how the mind creates an individual's reality. This is excellent news. Now that we know we can use our minds to affect our body chemistry, all we have to do is modify our thoughts. Surely a peaceful walk on the beach is preferable to a nightmare, and a pain-free life preferable to the agony of headaches. Of course, success requires developing a keen awareness of the dynamics and messages that travel between the mind and body. But nothing can be more rewarding than discovering the marvelous orchestration occurring within your being. It's worth every effort to listen to these harmonies.

Biofeedback is a relative of guided imagery. The term "biofeedback" is derived from "bio," meaning life, and "feedback" refers to the relay of information back to the subject. The feedback can come through self-observation or biofeedback equipment. When technology is used, sensors are attached to specific points on the body. The individual is then guided by auditory and visual cues that identify how thoughts change one's physiology. For example, envisioning one's feet in front of a crackling fire moves blood from overtaxed vessels in the head to the feet, reducing head pain. With a little practice, an individual can lower her blood pressure—also helpful for reducing headaches.

Neuro biofeedback specializes in mapping the brain, then boosting performance in any imbalanced areas through brain training sessions that utilize highly sophisticated technology. Brain training can have profound and lasting improvements on conditions like anxiety, depression, PTSD, ADHD, memory loss, and, of course, headaches.

After you have trained your brain, learned to redirect your mind, and tuned into your physiological responses, you may want to invest in a personal, portable biofeedback device to further nudge your physiology toward a healthy, restful state.

Changing habits is not always easy. Mental and behavioral modification requires effort, and mastery comes with practice. But awareness of one's mental, emotional, and physical responses plays a central role in eliminating headaches. The ability to take possession of your mind outfits you with a personal headache disintegrator.

CD's, DVD's, audio downloads, apps, and videos provide easy access to guided mental journeys. Just remember that the impact of the messages can be substantial, and you'll want to research your sources carefully, because subliminal messages can be laced into recordings—some constructive, some unfriendly. But let there be no doubt—introducing positive, relaxing images into the mind is priceless medicine for anyone—especially anyone experiencing headaches.

29

WHAT'S IN
YOUR WORLD?

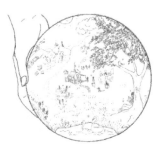

Set your life on fire. Seek those who fan your flames.

Rumi

Draw a circle on a piece of paper, then place a dot in the circle representing each person, situation, and factor that affects your life today. When you are finished, step back and take a proud look, for you have just constructed a snapshot of your current life.

When I first did this exercise, I used a blue dot to represent each positive aspect of my world (loving people, mountain hikes, pottery class, yoga) and a red dot to represent each troubling aspect (headaches, crazy-making boyfriend, the nightly news, a slowly dying mother). Drawing this simple version of reality helped me see matters clearly and identified the changes I needed to make. Once I became aware of the impact of negative friends and circumstances, those people were relocated to a position outside the circle. Eventually, they disappeared from my life. Give this exercise a try. I promise it will reveal something important to you.

As you adjust the people, places, and things in and around your circle, remember that there is no need to feel guilty if you relocate someone or something from the interior to the exterior of your circle. You can position people a healthy distance from your inner circle and still love them. As you consider each placement, it may help to remember that everything in life is contagious: kindness, integrity, honesty, beauty, healthy eating habits, lying, complaining, whining, sloppiness, victimization. So, in a very real sense, your placements reveal your inner desires—your choices.

Belongings can also trigger physiological responses. A tour of the items inside your home (rugs, lamps, vases, books, clothes, jewelry, furniture, keepsakes) will reveal your feelings about each object because the body's responses are visceral. Some reactions may be subtle, but with a little practice, you can identify which items conjure positive feelings and support health (need to stay) and which items bring negative, headache-causing associations (need to go).

The energy of emotions and thoughts also hangs out in physical spaces. How do you feel when you are in your home? Do some rooms feel better than others? Why? What about your office? Your car? How can you improve your spaces? Do you like the feeling of being in a library? A trash dump? A cathedral? When you tune in and find the answers to your questions, trust your instincts, and make the necessary changes. Even a small modification can have a sizable impact.

Space-clearing is an ancient practice that inspires us by cleansing energies and objects in our homes, offices, and other spaces. People from many walks of life, from Native Americans to the Pope, burn herbs, grasses, and spices to purify space. If it's sacred to Native Americans and clears the nooks and crannies of the Vatican, I trust it to cleanse my home.

Smoke, fire (candles), water, clapping, rocks, salt, essential oils, sage, and gemstones can also be used to shift the energy of a house or building. The central element in space clearing is intention. Setting an intention is like praying—it sends powerful messages outward and inward and builds a solid foundation for creating the life you want.

When your space feels good, you feel good, so when an important event is about to happen, clear your space. When something unpleasant has occurred, clear your space.

Here is an example of using sage and smoke to cleanse the energy of your home. You will first need to protect birds and other animals by removing them from the areas you are clearing. Smoke can set off smoke alarms, so you will want to prepare accordingly.

This clearing method requires a bundle of sage that has been collected by an uplifting person (keep everything positive), matches or a lighter, and a fireproof dish that's easy to hold.

- Light one end of the bundle of sage.
- After the sage flames, smudge-out the fire in the dish so the end of the bundle is only smoking—no fire.

⊘ Stand at the entrance to your house with the smoking sage stick and bowl. If you are in the northern hemisphere, walk clockwise along the perimeter of each room (reverse the direction in the southern hemisphere). Pay attention to areas where the air feels thick, heavy, or stagnant. Allow the smoke to drift into corners and roll under furniture. Waft it with your hand, a hand-held fan, or a feather.

⊘ Focus your thoughts, desires, and prayers upward and outward to the Creator of the universe. Connect to the Great Mystery, Jesus, Mother Nature, Angels, Ancestors—your words for God. Use your heart. Use your mind to release all negativity from your space, possessions, and your self.

⊘ When you have finished clearing your space, put your hands to your heart and say thank you to the forces that are helping you. Finish with a gesture—raise your hands to the sky.

⊘ After the clearing, invite sweet experiences and energies into your space. (Sweetgrass is often burned for this purpose.)

If space clearing with fire and smoke seems too daunting, purification can be accomplished with water, clapping, bells, salt, stones, words, and by simply focusing your intention. If these practices feel awkward for you, create your own ritual. The true goal of ceremony is to intentionally set your world right. Ritual is a form of prayer that clarifies the choice to invite the sacred into your life—you can do it any way you choose.

Improvements can be made to our lives by simple means: clean, polish, plant—make something better; lift away the excess, clear out, get rid of anything with *ick* on it. Consider the places you visit. Do they bring lightness and joy? Do novel experiences make your spirit soar? (Technically, they launch a dose of energizing dopamine into your system.)

An uncomplicated way to add positive elements to your world is to enrich someone else's life. That may sound kitschy, but it's true. Anonymously pay for a stranger's lunch or leave flowers at a neighbor's door, then pay attention to how you feel afterward. Altruistic actions cause positive chemical changes to the brain and body and are among your best headache-fighting allies.

Remember, you can make adjustments to that circle of positive and negative dots anytime. The more you review where you stand and who and what stands beside you, the more clarity you will gain. Your clear vision will show the way to wise choices that eliminate factors that cause harm and headaches. We choose what we want to include in our lives in the same way we select foods on a buffet. Some choices make us healthy. Others give us indigestion and headaches.

Look forward to the day you realize how good you feel—how your health and life have improved. You may even be surprised to find that the headaches are long-gone.

30

THE OPPOSITE
OF PERFECTION

Everybody is a genius. But if you judge a fish by its ability to climb a tree, it will live its whole life believing that it is stupid.

Albert Einstein

The opposite of perfectionism is not the opposite of perfect. "Perfect" is what you were the day you were born. Perfectionism is an externally acquired habit that produces pressure and is based in fear. Understanding the difference between the two is elemental to letting go of headaches and seeing yourself as the exquisite, happy person you really are.

I spent many years of my life trying to live up to the great expectations handed to me, with the best intentions, by family, friends, relatives, school, church, and the culture of the South in which I was raised.

I was a competitive gymnast (Junior Olympics) and an apt tennis player. I played the piano (terrifying recitals), was artistic and creative. I was a ranked Black Belt while I was still a Red Belt. I danced in a dance company. I sang in a quartet. I wrote poems. I was the president of my class. I owned a software company and won awards for educational youth programming. Yet after all of that, when my father died, I found myself standing on the end of a pier overlooking Pensacola Bay choking out an apology: "I tried, Daddy. I tried." I was heartbroken because I had failed to be what I thought he wanted me to be—perfect—never having made a mistake. No wonder I had headaches. I suspect my father's spirit was hovering beside me, desperately trying to straighten out my lopsided thinking.

Americans tend to applaud perfectionism. Overwork is glorified, and multitasking is presented as a positive trait even though it's scientifically proven to be detrimental to productivity and health. Although I enjoyed every activity I undertook and excelled at many, deep in my psyche, a little voice never stopped whispering, *Not good enough. You can do more. You can do better.*

How can we remove the lid from our culturally-stoked pressure cookers? What does it mean to be good enough— the best? The best quarterback, dancer, cook? What about the prettiest woman, handsomest man? What defines beauty, talent, usefulness? Is being an elder better than being young? Being younger better than being elder? All phases of life carry great gifts. Judgments are not helpful when freeing ourselves from the clutches of perfectionism and its de-energizing friends—strife and depression. I mean, who *wouldn't* have a headache.

Advertising and marketing certainly do their part to promote perfectionism. Marketers collaborate with social psychologists to design ad campaigns for products, from toilet paper to makeup, that target our dollars by creating and encouraging insecurities; they tell us we are not good enough. We don't have the latest gadget. Our car is old. We have wrinkles. Of course, the toys and airbrushed faces they're dangling in front of us aim to have us hang our heads in shame and fork over our money in an effort to measure up.

Straight hair was in vogue when I was a teenager. My hair was curly, so I tried to flatten it with a hot clothes iron. In reality, my curly hair was a part of the real me. I don't even look good with straight hair. As an adult, childhood friends later told me how much they had always loved my curly hair! All that angst for nothing.

When we let go of trying to be something we are not, we are rewarded with soul-nourishing relief. Being our authentic selves brings freedom, the kind of freedom we feel when we are alone on a mountain with no one there to judge us. If our goal is to live genuinely, why would we hurt ourselves with unkind, narrow decrees?

Every creature arrives on Earth bearing elaborate gifts. In a world of exquisite complexity, how can there be one "best"? To create a peaceful life and world, we have to widen our views and celebrate differences. Possibilities. When we replace judgment with inclusion, we take the heat off—the kind of heat that clamps down our energy, freezes our souls, and causes headaches.

After my Southwestern trip, I took a job in Santa Fe working for the New Mexico Supreme Court. One day, unsure about my choice of clothes, I stopped at the desk of a co-worker and asked, "Does this sweater look okay with this skirt?"

The woman looked up from her desk with a blank expression on her face. I repeated the question, and she uttered, "I guess so. It looks fine."

When I passed her door an hour later, I stopped once again and repeated my question. "Are you *sure* this looks okay?"

She stared a moment, then said one of the most curt and helpful things I have ever heard: "Elizabeth. Nobody cares." *Well! How rude!* Now, decades later, I wish I could remember her name so I could thank her for the little swat. Her honesty helped me recognize my self-focused perfectionism.

Changes in my nit-picky habits occurred slowly, but I was treated to evidence of my transformation one early morning when I discovered I was out of milk. I dressed quickly, and as I scurried out the door, I caught my reflection in a mirror. *Whoa!* There I stood, dressed in green, black, and red plaid flannel pants, topped with a double-breasted pink and yellow plaid flannel shirt. I looked like a clown. I burst out laughing with the realization that, *Hey, I've arrived!* I had dropped another piece of the extreme perfectionism that had held me hostage all of my life. (I did change my shirt before heading to the store.)

I encourage you to use the key to your own perfection-prison cell because the clutches of superficial fear reach much further than clothes. They generate chronic tension and, of course, headaches.

Stop asking other people if *you* are okay. Check with yourself instead. When we are clear about what's motivating our behaviors, we unearth our personal authority. The world needs your talents and joy. Isn't it time you recognize and treasure your value?

Sometimes growth arrives in unexpected ways. One of the best things I ever did was fail publicly. During a time of personal metamorphosis, I attended Unity of Boulder church in Colorado, where I undertook a year-long program: *A Course in Miracles* (ACIM). The class included a collection of students ranging from new seekers to wizened yogis. My participation required a forty-minute round trip between Longmont and Boulder, during which I sang to a Jackson Browne CD at the top of my lungs. After six months of the lyrical commute, my voice flowed as if I were ready for Lincoln Center.

Halfway through the course, I had to return to Florida. I felt so sad about leaving my community in Boulder that I decided to thank my fellow seekers by performing my rendition of my favorite Jackson Browne song: *For a Dancer.* Because I was afraid to sing alone, I opted to sing accompanied by the CD.

After my last ACIM class, forty-five classmates sat in chairs or cross-legged on the floor, their faces attentively waiting for me to begin my melodic goodbye. After positioning the CD player on a table beside me, I expressed my gratitude for their comradeship, pushed play, and opened my throat to sing. The first seven syllables came out okay, but without warning, my throat clamped down, transforming my song into squeaks punctuated by an occasional identifiable word. My body, confused by my ineptness, compensated by initiating an uncontrollable side-to-side sway, reminiscent of an enormous clock pendulum. In an attempt to regain a degree of decorum, I forced myself to stand still, which is when my ankles buckled.

After the minutes it took to croak out this song (sway, stop, buckle, sway, stop, buckle), half of the audience fled, while the other half appeared to be too stunned to leave. Despite the appalling performance, several nice things came of it. (That's how we headache people must learn to think.) A young woman took my hands in hers, gazed into my eyes, and said, "Thank you, *so much*. You have shown me that you don't have to be good at something to do it." I wasn't quite sure what to say, so I said thank you.

Later, I was rather proud of myself for going through with it even though I was petrified. As it turned out, losing control and doing a *lousy* job was real growth for me. I know that doesn't sound fun, but it was an awesome experience in what-the-hell.

One day a few years later in Florida, my mom called me to the phone. "Someone from Boulder wants to talk to you." It turned out to be a woman who had witnessed my singing goodbye. She had called to tell me how much my dreadful performance meant to her—how it gave her the courage to step out, try some things—make changes in her life. *Wow.* How's that for validation?

I learned several things from my first experience with public "failure." First, I don't know how my actions affect others. Second, I saw, in big letters, how terrified I was to show my real self. It's not like I didn't have experience singing and performing in front of people. I had given speeches for years. I'd excelled in a variety of public endeavors. But faced with exposing my *heart*, afraid of being misunderstood when revealing my raw and trembling self, I was so terrified that my body went berserk. Now *that* was indispensable information because if I ever wanted to be happy and lose the headaches, I needed to examine the underpinnings of the beliefs that undermined me.

I had my work cut out for me, and I was willing to tackle that work.

Any discussion about perfection includes a conversation about judgment. Perhaps everyone can relate to feeling inferior, but superiority is just inferiority in a fancy costume. I personally battle with the rotten habit of thinking I know more than other people. To hear me tell it, I am right, and everyone who disagrees with me is wrong. Oh, I behave nicely, but underneath, I'm thinking: *this person is just not evolved, that guy is driving too slowly, this woman just loves to hear herself talk, this poor guy is simply not intelligent.* Seriously? If you read that paragraph carefully, you'll see how harshly I judged *myself.* Judgment's sneaky like that. It's a mean liar. It critiques and critiques and critiques, and every analysis is unfair. Inaccurate.

There is no such thing as "right" or "wrong." What do I know about the slow driver? Maybe the guy is not trying to annoy me; maybe it's his first day on the road after recovering from a stroke. And, of course, my poisonous thoughts don't just fill the air with ill will, they also poison my body—my life. They cause headaches. Why would I want to do that?

Putting the mind in reverse is a useful tactic when addressing perfectionistic thinking because if I am judging *you*, I clearly do not feel good about *me*. In the process of judging, I am injuring both of us. This is not a goal to which I aspire, so when I catch my mind misbehaving, I call on my loving side. I extend a thought of apology to the person I judged, God, myself, and the world. I make myself work. I say, "I take it back," and picture a big eraser wiping the negative thought out of my mind. Then I send a blessing. Maybe I think of the person as if they are my mother, father, brother, or friend; I acknowledge that this individual could be the stranger that might stop and help me with a flat tire. Then I hold them in my heart: *May you have all good things. Peace, joy, love, health. May Angels light your way. Amen.*

What happens next is important: I ask myself why I am so cranky. And with that crucial question, I begin to look in a place where I might actually find an answer—within myself. Maybe I'll answer honestly and say *because my life isn't like I want it to be.* Okay, good. Now I'm getting somewhere. Now, I can dig into the details. *How do I want my life to be?* When I configure a clear answer to this all-important question by using my tools (like writing, vision-boarding, talking, meditating), I am so busy creating the life I want that there's no time for complaining, anger, or headaches. I feel happy. Generous. I think differently. I value the man with low intelligence and honor the talkative woman. I even let the slow driver slide ahead of me as we approach the entrance ramp onto the highway.

#31

WORDS & MIND TALK

A man is what he thinks about all day long.

Ralph Waldo Emerson

There is a scene in the film *Alice in Wonderland* when Alice, dressed in armor, is preparing to meet the terrifying Jabberwocky. Alice is small and the Jabberwocky is forty feet tall—all savage teeth and roar. Fortunately, Alice inherited a powerful habit from her father: "Sometimes, I believe in as many as six impossible things before breakfast." Because of her belief, experience, and determination, she drew her sword and walked toward the Jabberwocky, pumping herself up by reciting her six seemingly unbelievable things: "One! There is a potion that can make you shrink. Two! A cake that can make you tall . . ." Alice finishes the list with number six: "I can slay the Jabberwocky." Because she believes her words, she is victorious in slaying her nemesis. Despite the world's need for non-aggression, the film provides an excellent example of the power of self-talk.

Positive self-talk is an invaluable skill, taught by many

students of humanity like Norman Vincent Peale (*The Power of Positive Thinking*), Andrew Weil, MD (*Spontaneous Healing*), and numerous current cognitive psychologists. Great thinkers and sages from Sophocles to Einstein have referenced the power of mystery, belief, words, and thoughts. The mind, it seems, is the factory where all good or crummy things are made.

Because the mind bears distinctive elements, an understanding of the difference between ego-mind and the authentic nature of a person can provide priceless, headache-busting insights. Friedrich Nietzsche, Ram Dass, and countless other notables became both students and teachers in the field of differentiating ego from the true nature of the self.

Ego-mind is mental chitter-chatter, a collection of stories, resentments, and mental noise; it can easily lead us into reactivity. One's *true* nature has a quiet presence with no need to be flashy.

Ego can actually *help* an individual by sounding warning bells when danger is present, but ego-mind can also bang out warning signals when there is no danger. This reaction prevents calm, appropriate action and engulfs the body with headache fuel—adrenaline. *Authentic* mind is *knowing* and leads to wise choices and serenity. Hearing this helpful voice requires being still long enough to watch the superficial narrative in the mind and see it for the impostor it is. Successfully switching the mind from the horror movie channel to *WW-Happy* occurs when we allow ourselves to experience emotions, then let any churned-up emotional pond scum disperse. After the water clears, we can set our sights on loftier goals and *respond* rather than react. When we realize our emotions are like nuclear power plants, we can observe them as they wash through us instead of letting them initiate a crisis. We remain calm instead of reactively hitting the big, red "Push Here for Headache" button.

Many students of peace create books and videos highlighting the importance of using the mind wisely. Author Robin Sharma tells us that "The mind is a wonderful servant but a terrible master." Indeed. The good news is we can train ourselves to be the master and live in a state of calm observation and personal power.

The book, *The Law of Attraction*, by Esther and Jerry Hicks, and the film of the same name, provide worthwhile information about the habituted mind and its magnetic capability to attract the object of its focus.

Dr. Masaru Emoto proved the power of words, thoughts, and music with his mind-boggling water crystal experiment (1994), which gained fame as *The Message of Water*.

In his study, Dr. Emoto placed a variety of labels on containers filled with water. Some vessels were marked with damaging words like "I hate you; I am going to kill you." Other bottles were labeled with loving words: "You are wonderful; I love you." Then he played music, meditated, and prayed the sentiments written on the label toward the water before freezing it.

Remarkably, the water (crystals) exposed to positive language and thoughts transformed into organized, symmetrical patterns similar to snowflakes. The water exposed to negativity transformed into disfigured shapes. Because our bodies are primarily made of water, we implicitly understand that if we can modify the structure of water, we can promote our health by using constructive words and thoughts.

During the worst of my headache years, I was traumatized by the headaches themselves. My mind and body learned to brace themselves in preparation for each ensuing headache. My thoughts were about headaches, and the more I feared and expected headaches, the more they came to me. That is not to discount other factors, but to emphasize that if all other elements are aligned with health, and I continue to focus on headaches, headaches will come.

When I learned to concentrate on productive, life-encouraging endeavors, I began to release old negative patterns and attract positive experiences. Those emancipating experiences were contagious—they made me laugh, and I wanted more of them.

Speaker and transformational counselor, Robert Wegin, agrees that healing the body is about God, prayer, and the power of thinking. Wegin tells us that the body is endowed daily with 500,000 healthy new cells that await our instructions. In other words, our thoughts, words, and beliefs direct the behavior of our cells.

It's important to let go of "I'm right" thinking. Rather than saying, "I have bad lungs," or "I have bad digestion," we can direct new cells to create health: "I am healthy and happy and strong. Your job today, New Cells, is to epitomize health and convert unhealthy cellular structures into happy, healthy cells."

I believe in saying thank you, too.

Our personal stories about life and events can keep us mentally, emotionally, and physically stuck. Fortunately, we can replace unloving thoughts, words, and actions with their positive counterparts and produce healthy body chemistry, resulting in positive actions that are remarkably easy to accomplish.

Tip the drive-through clerk at a fast-food restaurant. Read or write a list of positive words and statements. Tell someone why you love them. Just shift the mind and body into a positive narrative and feeling state: *I am healthy. I am talented. I am grateful for my magnolia tree, good friends, my cat, dog, two legs, children, water, my car, mother nature, feathers, dolphins, fresh air, money, bugs, good vision, monkeys, hope.* With practice, positive thoughts occur with ease.

Since words create reality, it may be a good idea to avoid talking about headaches. After all, if we talk about them, people will *ask* us about them. *How's your head?* The last thing you need is to be reminded that you are supposed to have a headache. Inform friends and family of your quest to reorient your thinking toward positive subjects and away from headaches. Enlist their help. Ask them to inquire about your new job, your violin lessons, that book you started, the project you finished—things that make you happy and strong. If you find yourself centering conversations around headaches, it may be useful to ask yourself *why*. Is there a secret you need to share? Is the only way you can get much-needed attention to be in pain? (If yes, consider how to get attention elsewhere.) Are you miserable in your current job and don't know how to tell your spouse, so you conjure headaches to do your talking? Are you afraid to step into the unknown? (Could the unknown possibly be worse than having headaches?)

Welcome all questions, and trust that honest answers lead to supportive actions and freedom.

Headaches are good teachers, and you are a good student who can let headaches go and embrace the life you desire.

32

UNLOCKED EMOTIONS

You can't heal what you can't feel.

John Bradshaw

Emotions are a wondrous part of being human, unless we stifle them, in which case they become squatters in the soul. Repressed emotions are remarkably accommodating while waiting for their chance to express themselves—the rascals simply refuse to leave until they get their turn. Stuck emotions often campaign for our attention through physical ailments. Fortunately, humans possess an inner physician who knows how to remove the chains of emotional stagnation and release tension in productive ways.

Basically, humans are spirits with worldly components, and one aspect of our worldliness involves a propensity for gathering information. As a matter of fact, the "record" switch is turned on before we are born. Even in utero, sights, sounds, smells, tastes, and experiences are recorded in our beings and brains as soon as our neurons develop. A parent who says, "Oh, she's too young to know what I am saying," or "Oh, he's too young to know what happened," is misinformed.

Infants, children, and adults record everything—faces, scenes on televisions, and interactions between people gossiping in the living room. A baby may not be able to interpret or verbalize exactly what is said but is nonetheless keenly aware of everything in the environment. Once grown to adulthood, that person may not consciously remember childhood events and emotions but can *feel* them. The feelings remain ensnarled in the mind and body, impacting perceptions, experiences, and physicality. Finding freedom from headaches requires recognizing, acknowledging, and expressing such emotions.

The power packed by my emotions has always been over-sized. It's a trait born from my need to be perfect, amplified by a cultural mandate to *always* be a kind, loving lady. Too bad my interpretation of being ladylike resulted in an excess of politeness and deferential behaviors which prohibited the expression of less "pretty" feelings. The result? Inner conflict.

When anger or frustration overtook me, my mother would say, "You just need to get control of your emotions!" It took a long time to grasp that concept, and I still wrangle with finding a balance between over-expression and *no* expression. These days, when unexpressed feelings go for a romp beneath my ribs, I know how to handle them, but before I did a lot of healing work, suppressed emotions caused massive tension and headaches. Even now, whenever I become righteously indignant, physiological changes immediately make themselves known, threatening to create a headache. My awareness and desire for a headache-free life allow me to recognize my reactivity, calm my system, and avoid headaches.

My stay at the Diamond Headache Clinic included an art therapy class. The therapist was a gentle woman who introduced us to the concept of illustrating our headaches. The mere prospect of uncovering the unnamed, invisible *thing* that had been striking me down for years rendered me both eager and terrified. A powerful silence pervaded the room as each of us mustered our courage and coaxed our headaches out where we could get a good look at them.

I still remember where I was sitting in the classroom (in the back), the feel of the cold surface of the table, the sweet smell of the crayons. My breathing became shallow and my throat clamped down before I could scrape the first stroke across the paper. With blood-pumping apprehension, I let each color—black swirls, jagged red strikes—fly onto the page. Out came the ambiguous depression, the hellish jabs, the blindsiding attacks and brutality. Anger. Frustration. *Damn headaches. I was so afraid of them.* And yet, the headaches were a part of me—*came* from me. The drawing was showing me something—many things. Could I see them? And then, there they were: my headaches.

In the only colors natural to headache anguish, red and black, I beheld my story in picture form. The longer I stared at the drawing, the more I saw. The image seemed to change with every viewing—the deeper I looked, the more truth wafted up from the page: causes, negative habits, the pressure and guilt I'd felt over not being able to overcome my affliction.

When the headache drawings were completed, we were asked to draw what we would do if we didn't have headaches. My happy-place featured myself as a stick figure, silly smile on my face, paddling a canoe down a tree-lined stream. I remember how pathetic it seemed that my big aspiration was to paddle a canoe without fear of a headache or the need to carry a waterproof baggie of pain pills.

The room remained quiet as each of us stood and shared images of our headaches and dreams. One woman drew a figure holding a flowerpot and a trowel: "I just want to be able to work in my garden." Another woman illustrated herself on a boat with two young children: "I want to go on a trip with my grandchildren." Every story accessed vats of compassion for these women and for *myself.*

Art therapy held tremendous clarifying effects for me, and I continued to draw headaches for years. The images helped me figure out what the headaches were trying to tell me. As I became increasingly fluent in processing emotions, I developed new methods of "seeing" my feelings.

In a fit of fury and sorrow involving a collection of troubles—my mother's dementia, headaches, a challenging boyfriend, a crazy-making job—I set up a 4 x 6-foot canvas in my living room, where I immediately began to paint.

I let go of all thinking, grabbed a tube of black paint and forcefully squished it straight from the tube onto the upper left corner of the canvas. I circled the brush, scrubbing, until the pigment transformed into a spiraling dark hole. Driven by emotion and instinct, I added dark blue, painting shapes over the black, and I kept moving the colors around. Indigo circles became pocked with thick black lines. As I worked, I realized that not only was I expressing myself, the paint was talking to *me.*

What did that corner of the canvas show me? I was black and blue with sorrow about my mother's situation. The black hole pulled me in, revealing the depth of a depression I felt but had not admitted.

Moving to the next blank space on the canvas, I squeezed out a chaotic mélange of red, green, black, and grey—my soul telling me about my troublesome job—*See your outrage, your fury, Elizabeth? Your self-battering insistence on keeping this job?* Yes. I saw it. (It still took me a while to take action.) As I laid my troubles on the canvas, I began to understand my situation. *Ahhh! I see!* The clarity helped me release blocked feelings and move toward solutions.

Another painting, which represented my boyfriend, took a month to complete. During that time, the canvas became an ever-changing piece of furious red and black art. I'd throw a brush loaded with red paint at it on a Monday and slice it with a sterling silver fork on Thursday. I'd bellow and add more paint every time I found myself in a negative situation. The habit of expressing emotion through art and appropriate action proved invaluable and helped me extricate myself from the predicament *and* the unhealthy relationship.

You may be thinking, *Man, healing my emotions is going to take forever!* Clearing old emotional ick is indeed a process. We all want a fast solution, but I promise that the growth and benefits of doing *your* personalized tango with issues and their accompanying emotions are worth it. This is about your *life.*

Just give it a try.

Give it your best try.

During the headache years, vacations, outings, and endeavors took place under the threat of a headache, and I didn't go anywhere without arming myself with prescription meds. I participated in life despite head pain, but pressing forward in pain produced more tension. More headaches. Worse headaches. One headache was so horrific I was hospitalized. Even I.V. drugs could not eliminate the excruciating pain. Deep within, I knew why.

Trauma comes in as many forms as there are people. There are two basic types: Big-T (like seeing a friend blown up by a landmine) and Little-T (like repeatedly being told you are bad or stupid). Trauma can be subtle and slow-moving, occurring over time, or it can happen suddenly. It involves things seen, heard, or experienced physically, spiritually, emotionally, and mentally. The nature of the distress is immaterial, and the affected person is the only one who knows why an event was so painful and life-altering. Some traumas are obvious, while some are so subtle we are not even aware of them. A child innocently singing under a tree can be traumatized by someone making fun of him—affecting him for life.

In my case, the trauma was sudden, and it ramped up my previously healthy stress level to Mach 5. Making matters worse, I didn't tell anybody what happened to me, so an avalanche of emotions and negative images stored themselves in the hidden closets of my psyche. Secrets are bad news, and opening the valve to healing requires either time, courage and wisdom, *or* pain so amplified that keeping them locked up becomes intolerable.

After seventeen years of demoralizing headaches, I was breaking, so I installed myself in a cutting-edge therapeutic center. I intended to get to the bottom of any emotional causes of the headaches. The program involved experiential groups that helped me unearth, replay, and speak up about issues from my past. Each participant revisited old wounds through role-playing with members of the group, re-enacting traumatizing events. It was a serious business facilitated by well-trained professional psychotherapists.

One evening my head hurt so badly I left my room and walked down the outdoor walkway toward the nurses' station to request an injection. As I walked along, I remembered how much I wanted to be free of headaches and prescription medications—free from an addiction to pain, so I turned back toward my room, but before I got there, I turned around again, thinking, *No, this hurts too much.* I was still walking back and forth, deliberating, when a therapist named Mike walked toward me and asked how I was doing. Scrunching my face, I answered, "I have a really bad headache."

Mike stopped, and said, "You *are* a headache, Elizabeth." Even though Mike's comment admittedly pumped some anger-related adrenaline into my bloodstream, I later appreciated his audacity and insight. Most of my life *did* revolve around headaches: being afraid of them, treating them, planning for them, searching for solutions, preparing ice bags, refreezing gel packs. Indeed, headaches took up most of my life, even when I was having "fun." Yahoo.

After I began to speak up about past events, fear, anger, and shame, the internal pressure began to dissipate. I was emboldened to take each ensuing step, unearthing deep questions and finding answers. Some burdens dissolved slowly while others dispersed rapidly. Having a support system during my recovery was imperative.

As I related earlier, I had a happy childhood. Safe. Innocent. So I was completely unprepared to deal with the "Big-T" trauma that struck at age nineteen. The trauma was so sudden, so deep, it replaced my previously healthy physical state with extreme muscle tension and mangled my previously calm demeanor. Because I kept the trauma secret, by the time I entered the therapeutic center, I was dealing with multiple traumas piled with an accumulation of anger, blame, terror, and shame. I also had to address my habit of putting on a happy face and realize that ignoring my emotions was a sham that was screwing up my life. What a woeful waste of a perfectly fine existence. In the end, I had to grieve, belatedly, for that happy-go-lucky girl who morphed into a braced, tight pillar of tension.

The staff at the healing center was so proficient they knew precisely how to address my wounds. When they asked my group of twelve, "Who would like to do some healing work today?" my hand was the first to shoot into the air. The counselors asked me to share my story, then used the group to sculpt and re-enact the events surrounding the trauma. Even though the scene played out my greatest fears, I was able to trust the therapists and find a sense of resolution, which took years of work to fully integrate. With professional support, I took that crucial first step toward resolving my first, seemingly mortal wound.

Taking one step, then another, no matter how slow or tentative, eventually cleared my vision so I could stop being hard on myself and others. Now, I understand my behavioral makeup and view my life as the spiritual journey it has always been. The naked truth did, indeed, set me free and continues to do so.

My hidden emotions took time and effort to resolve, but when I healed the past, my feet found their rhythm on the highway to happiness. I only wish I had started walking down that road sooner. The key is to begin—to do one little thing to free the pressure of emotional lockdown. Sometimes we are only able to put one toe in the water. Sometimes we feel strong enough to dive in. Just pay attention to your needs and do *something*. Doodle. Ride a bike. Write a letter. Plan a trip. Move your mind, your soul, your body, your heart. Open up. Find someone to trust and start talking. Learn what you need to learn. You have all of the questions and are the only one with the answers. And remember, courage is the ability to face and move through fear, as opposed to the impossibility of "overcoming" it. Fear's not scary when you shake hands with it. You may even detect a congratulatory smile on its face.

As we heal and let the fresh waters of positive experiences pour back into our souls, it is imperative to stop the flow of incoming negativity. Welcome positive people, places, and things; allow negative people, places, and things to go elsewhere.

Remember, emotions are based upon perception, and perception is something we can control. Although we can't control the world and many events, we *can* control how we interpret and react to them. We just have to be honest—sit still, feel our emotions, and consider alternate views. Expressed emotions do not harm us. Stifled emotions do.

As our perception of hurtful events changes, we remember how to relax and return to an inner strength that lives inside each of us. We develop gratitude for everyone who reminds us to seek answers from within. Our divergent paths to truth and peace are ours alone, and each individual must find their own trail through the forest.

By unlocking our emotions, we banish judgment—including self-judgment, and as we scrape off the dirt and crud of our pasts, we begin to shine. We eliminate the ick and reveal our beauty.

We let go and heal.

We allow headaches to fall away.

#33

KINDNESS

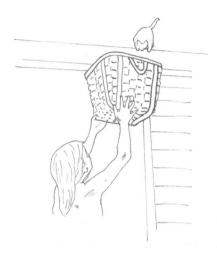

I am larger, better than I thought;
I did not know I held so much goodness.

Walt Whitman

Kindness is an elixir for headache sufferers; it improves the chemistry of the brain and issues a passport to the elimination of headaches. In fact, studies show that all forms of kindness carry a positive influence—just *observing* an act of kindness increases serotonin, the "happy life" neurotransmitter in the brain. Technically, the process occurs via specialized brain cells called "mirror neurons." From neurophysiologist Giacomo Rizzolatti we know that "Mirror neurons allow us to understand other people's minds, not only through conceptual reasoning but through imitation. Feeling, not thinking." Fortunately, it's easy to use mirror neurons to our advantage because igniting the benefits of kindness is as simple as watching a happy movie or calling a lonely neighbor.

Paying it forward is a powerful form of kindness. I once pulled up to a coffeehouse drive-through window and the cashier said, "The car in front of you paid your bill." I felt such joy I paid for the person in line behind me. Paying it forward isn't always about money—your positivity can be currency; if you thank the store clerk for his cheerful customer service, it will carry through his day and *yours*.

It is, indeed, reassuring to know that the kindness I show someone else raises my spirits and unleashes a stream of beneficial hormones into my body. After experiencing the updraft induced by random acts of kindness, it's easy to become a kindness vending machine. Whether it's through a phone call, a compliment, or a genuine "thank you," I can make someone's day brighter while improving mine. And if other recipients of goodwill are anything like me, they will be inspired to pass the thoughtfulness on to others.

Even when we encounter angry people, we have a choice of behaviors. If we react to an unpleasant interaction with fear or anger, the brain signals the release of adrenaline and cortisol into our system. Those chemicals contribute to tension and headaches. Our responses automatically soften when we zoom out to a macro view and consider anger as a possible cry for love, extreme frustration, helplessness, or who knows what? It literally pays to avoid judging other people's reactions and emotions.

In choosing kindness, we also determine our opinion of ourselves. Do we laugh at the mean joke just because everyone else is laughing? Such moments define us and reveal what we think, want, and believe. To achieve good health, we must opt for behaviors we admire.

Admittedly, some interactions require us to take care of ourselves by speaking up. The answer to such situations is to step up while remaining compassionate—set a positive example. This kind of opportunity came to me at a fast-food restaurant in Colorado.

I was quietly writing in my journal when a commotion among a group of college students jolted me from my musings. I looked up to find everyone in the restaurant staring through the plate glass windows toward the drive-through exit lane. Three especially loud young men stood by the window, laughing at a driver who had mistaken the exit lane for the entrance. The driver, an elderly woman, was stuck. Whenever she put the car in reverse, she'd run into the curb. When she drove forward, a sharp curve in the driveway made matters worse.

Her distress was evident, and I was appalled by the heartless atmosphere in the restaurant. *Were these kids just going to watch this woman struggle?* As soon as the thought entered my mind, one of the laughing young men said, "I hope I'm never that stupid."

That did it for me. I stood up, quietly walked outside to the lady's car, and leaned down. (I knew the kids were watching.) "Are you stuck?" Yes, she was stuck. She smiled apologetically. "I don't know how I could have done this."

"Anyone could have done it," I said. "I can back it out for you if you like."

"I think I can do it," she said. "Thank you so much." And with just that smidgeon of kindness, she was able to back her car out with ease. I slowly walked back inside and sat down without looking at anyone. I hope the students decided that kindness was cooler than cruelty.

Still, what if you have to converse about a problem?

Let's say you have a friend who compulsively needs to be in control. You feel stressed-out when you're around her, yet, you keep accepting invitations to her house for lunch. Honest, yet gentle communication can free you both, regardless of the result of the conversation. Of course, sympathetic communication requires a clear, grounded mind and a calm, loving state of being. The beauty of effective communication is its ability to protect all parties from misunderstandings or holding grudges, both of which contribute to headaches and other afflictions.

Some situations are trickier than others, of course, which is when intuition and common sense serve as excellent guides. You may love your pet rattlesnake, but it's not a good idea to kiss him on the nose—same with venomous people.

Speaking and behaving kindly are staples in the psyche of happy, healthy humans. They are qualities that amp up personal power and generate a calmness that comes from knowing one can handle any situation with grace. It took a long time for me to realize how my frustration and lack of self-care were hurting me—for no good reason.

Take the simple case of a friend with a sailboat . . .

Brunie was trying to tie his boat to a dock when he discovered a knot in one of the ropes. A strong wind was blowing the boat away from the pier, and the line was too taut to untie the gnarl, so Brunie handed me the bowline and asked, "Would you walk the boat down the dock, then just hold it still?"

I felt strong and healthy, and wanted to help, so I said, "Sure!" and started pulling the boat forward using the rope. I soon realized the task required constant heavy pulling into the wind. Instead of speaking up: "Brunie, I think you're going to have to do this; it's hurting my neck," I continued to tug on the rope for twenty minutes. With a back shaped like a pretzel, the result was a strained neck and knotted shoulder muscles. I exacerbated the problem by going home and leaning toward my computer for three hours of online webinars. Result? Pain from hips to shoulders, and, of course, a headache. Lesson learned, albeit painfully. Brunie would have been perfectly happy to handle the boat, and I could easily have eliminated the webinars instead of pushing myself so hard.

The great news about awareness is we can learn from our observations and let them fine-tune future choices. We can be kind to *ourselves,* which promotes genuine care for others, and leaves us headache-free with plenty of room for happy, inspired endeavors.

34

PLAY

It is a happy talent to know how to play.

Ralph Waldo Emerson

Play is a natural healer and possesses an almost magical ability to create good health. It's headache repellant. Real, down-home play makes us laugh so hard that the brain sends happy juice (in the form of wellness hormones like dopamine, serotonin, oxytocin, and endorphins) throughout the body. No headache can survive spontaneous, rollicking laughter.

Adults often view play as childish, and our cultural programming steers us away from playfulness for fear of appearing foolish. What harsh judges we can be. In reality, childlikeness bathes the body in natural healing agents, so we are wise to let the child within us frolic in some old-fashioned fun.

Author and eternal optimist Norman Cousins believed in the power of natural healing and laughter. Norman had several existing health issues when he discovered he also had a degenerative spinal disease (and most-likely headaches). His solution was to put himself on a health regimen that included heavy doses of vitamin C, funny movies, comical television programs, and cartoons. He recorded his story of natural healing in his excellent autobiography, *Anatomy of an Illness*.

Is there an activity that throws you into fits of laughter? *Pictionary? Twister?* That's the kind of play we want. For me, it's fast card games, ping-pong, and tennis—I laugh like a goon when I miss the ball. Charades is also guaranteed to deliver a laughing fit—so is stealing a bite of someone's pie.

My mother and father liked each other, and they played a lot. Mama was washing dishes one morning when she spied Daddy watering the camellias outside the open kitchen window. Her fun side led the way, and she blasted him with the sink's spray hose. Daddy looked up, grinned, and doused her and half the kitchen with garden hose water. By the time I heard Mom's squeals and made it to the kitchen, the show was over. Just remembering that moment makes me smile.

My mom sometimes played construction assistant to my father. One day she helped him repair the living room ceiling. Daddy was standing on a scaffold, balancing a cumbersome piece of sheetrock on his head when I walked into the room. "Honey," he was saying to Mom, "Could you hand me that two-by-four?" I watched as Daddy willed the sheetrock into submission, simultaneously reaching a blind hand in Mom's direction. As my mother lifted the heavy board upward, she wobbled and cracked my father soundly on the shin. After one appalling moment, Mom fell into fits of laughter. Daddy, helpless with the sheetrock perched atop his head, put on a grand show of grimaces punctuated with high-pitched screeches that kept her going until tears of laughter were rolling down her face. My parents were masters at making emotional gold out of potentially not-so-funny situations.

Friends and family used to beg my brother, Anson, to stop telling stories (". . . so that old green car was still rolling down the hill, the yellow boat strapped to the top—no brakes, and the boat starts sliding, *heh-heh* . . .") because our aching stomach muscles couldn't take any more hilarity. *That* is the kind of laughter that heals. Good-natured, *haw, haw, haw* stuff.

You can invite a galaxy of health into your life by making a list of things that make you laugh, scheduling them on your calendar, and then *doing* them. Put the list in your car where you can see it. Tape it to your computer screen, your phone, your bathroom mirror. Read your list *every* morning, every night. And here's the most important part about scheduling playtime—it works if you keep your appointments.

My play list looks like this:

- Sit with a friend and say people's names backwards: "Enyogrub Yram. Htebazile Splehp."
- Draw pictures in the sand by the bay with my nephew Alexander, and watch my five-year-old niece, Morgan, run down the beach.
- Write with my opposite hand.
- Play goofy-golf.
- Hop in the car and go on an adventure to I don't know where.
- Walk in the rain.
- Make a clay pot.
- Ride go-carts.
- Play charades.

- Take an art class.
- Swim in the ocean.
- Play ping-pong or tennis.
- Play hopscotch, cards, chess, or checkers.
- Walk barefoot in the grass or on the beach.
- Go bowling.
- Watch comedians on television.
- Write "I love you" on the mirror with lipstick.
- Leave a surprise gift at a friend's front door.

Make your own play list, and remember to let life's goofy circumstances tickle you. Lighten-up and get busy unleashing those positive neurotransmitters!

Play and laugh. Then play and laugh some more.

It will heal you.

It will *am-scray* headaches. Promise.

#35

PRAYER

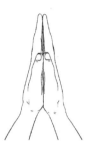

Work for God, love God alone, and be wise with God.
When an ordinary man puts the necessary rime and enthusiasm
into meditation and prayer, he becomes a divine man.

Paramahansa Yogananda

My parents taught me to say traditional bedtime prayers when I was three years old:

> *Now I lay me down to sleep*
> *I pray the Lord my soul to keep.*
> *Guide me through the starry night*
> *And wake me when the sun shines bright.*

As years passed, I tagged on personal prayer requests: "God bless Mama and Daddy and Anson and Edgar and Cocoa (the cat) and Papa and Grammy and Grandmother and the kittens and . . ."

My prayers took a while.

Church was a vital part of our family life and provided

strong building blocks for developing and fostering a thirst for understanding the operations behind God and prayer. Potent spiritual foundations were woven into our lives through nature, creativity, philosophical thinking, and the integrity of my parents. Days spent among flowers, bees, sunshine, and grass helped prepare the especially rich layer of spiritual topsoil in which I grew.

My concept of prayer expanded significantly one morning when my father sat at the kitchen table, pondering the nature of God. He said, "I wonder if God's like a big computer, hooked up to everything." At the time, the thought was novel because computers were uncommon in the seventies. My father's comment supported my experience with the connectivity of all things and inspired my curiosity. It also gave me permission to explore all possibilities.

As years passed, I discovered varieties of prayer and observed how they operated in my life. My friend, Ruthie, broadened my view during a conversation about spirituality (not religion) and prayer. I must have said something dense because, at one point, Ruthie looked at me dumbfounded, then emphasized, "Elizabeth, every *thought* is a prayer!" *Every thought? Yipe!* Not only did Ruthie's words ring true, they placed the responsibility of managing my mind where it belonged—on my own shoulders. The implications for headache release became clearer: observe, then direct thoughts toward a positive perception, because thoughts constantly affect one's life—and the lives of others.

I was pushing hard when I was age twenty-two. After work, I practiced karate, then went to my boyfriend's house; I consistently got home late. My face was breaking out. Headaches were slaying me.

One Saturday morning, I noticed my boyfriend's car parked at a local restaurant, so I went in to surprise him, only to find him engaged in some serious flirting with a woman he seemed to know a bit too well. I felt betrayed. Even though it was time for the relationship to end, I was too codependent to break up with him, so we argued until I went home. I was a ball of anxiety, hurt, and fury when I crawled into bed that night, and all I could do was sob and repeat, "God help me. God help me. God help me . . ." until, exhausted, I fell asleep. The next morning, I awakened happy. Clearly, something had happened during the night. My circumstances were the same—work environment, karate, inappropriate boyfriend, but I felt *absolute* peace. *Nothing* bothered me. Normally, I would have held onto my fury and fear, and agonized over every detail of the problem, so this newfound tranquility was a big deal. Instead of feeling devastated, I floated through the next seven days in a state of harmony and calm. Interestingly, the following Monday, *poof!* some mysterious switch flipped, and my mucked-up thinking and emotions returned. Nonetheless, the peace I had experienced during the week was so profound that it cemented my understanding of the power of absolute prayer and opened a world of new possibilities.

There were many more to come.

My headache hell peaked when I managed a team of therapists and teachers engaged in educating a special group of fourth-grade students. The movie, *Dances with Wolves*, had just been released, and it was the perfect vehicle for teaching character: integrity, honor, courage, friendship, compassion, and a healthy respect for beauty and nature. *Dances with Wolves* became the backdrop for the program.

During the planning phase, I described my ideas to my Native friend, Brunie, explaining my desire to develop activities and meaning inspired by his culture. He suggested I contact a Lakota medicine man from Rosebud Reservation in South Dakota. His name was Walter Littlemoon, and he happened to be visiting locally.

Walter agreed to see me.

Walter stood about six-foot-three and had shiny, long black hair. He sat sideways to me as I explained what I hoped to accomplish for our students. He never looked directly at me and remained silent even after I described my plan and shared my motivations. "I don't want to be another clueless white person teaching children about Native Americans." After an awkward moment, I asked, "Do you have any advice for me?"

He continued to look straight ahead, didn't move a muscle, then softly said, "You need to do a lodge."

"A lodge?"

Walter remained quiet, eyes forward, and gently repeated, "You need to do a lodge."

I did a lodge. Actually, I did five or six.

Aside from learning a little about Lakota culture, I discovered a lot about myself—like how overly-worried and impatient I was.

My first sweat lodge was scheduled to begin at sundown. It required a forty-five-minute drive, during which I stopped twice to deliberate whether to go or turn around and forget it. I had a *massive* headache. I finally stopped in a parking lot until I made a decision. As I sat there vacillating, I became aware that my current mental gymnastics epitomized the habits that prevented me from trusting life and doing things I wanted to do. I headed toward the lodge.

I arrived in the late afternoon with the attitude of a typical, busy white woman: *let's get the show on the road.* For the first hour and a half, I kept looking at my watch (who wears a watch to a sweat lodge?). I was thinking, *It's sundown! I thought we were starting at sundown?* To my credit, I eventually caught on and removed the watch.

As twilight turned toward night, about fifteen of us sat around an enormous fire. Everyone else was busy quietly making little colored pouches of tobacco. One of the women noticed that I was new and explained the purpose of the pouches and showed me how to make my own. I chose blue fabric for a pouch representing prayers to heal my brother Anson's waning eyesight, blue for comfort for my mom, green for the protection of the environment, and so on. As I made each pouch, I focused on my intentions—my prayers for specific people and situations. By the time I entered the lodge, I had traded my rush-rush mentality for a string of well-considered prayers I wore around my neck.

The spirit of the sweat lodge reminded me of going to church only with a long preparation phase and no concern for wardrobe. The benevolent man who led the lodge ensured that I sat beside him so he could give me a ladle of water if I needed it. I hung my prayer pouches on a willow branch that curved over my head, then sat still as the sacred, glowing hot stones were brought into the center of the lodge. Then came sage, water on the stones, and steam so hot I wondered if I could die from the heat. The fear served to intensify my prayers. Cultural and language differences held no significance; I sang songs in Lakota even though I didn't speak Lakota—and I instinctively knew what they meant. Because it was impossible to fall back on normal habits and words, my focus was total, and the sincerity of our circle of worshipers was so palpable we were unified even though we had been strangers only a few hours before.

After the ceremony, I felt purged, quiet, and spent—in a good way. My prayers had floated up with the smoke from the fire—so had my headache.

It was gone.

For me, prayers involve getting out of my own way. I have to let go of preconceived notions and surrender my aching emotions and bruised life, so that Spirit can move me forward with the methods it chooses. I always receive answers regardless of how I deliver my prayers, although some answers don't feel so good.

Let's use Lucy Smith as an example.

Lucy is a poet who yearns to make the world a better place. She aches for adventure because it drives her inspiration to share her heart through poetry. Lucy is wildly unhappy because she is very far from inspiration and writing poetry—she makes yoyo's in a factory six days a week.

One October day, a hurricane blows her apartment building down. Of course, Lucy's freaked out. But! Instead of moving into another apartment, and in spite of feeling sad, angry, and scared (with no idea how she'll pay for her life), Lucy rides life's unexpected waves. She quits her job, packs her bags, hops in her car, and starts driving. Adventure! When she reaches Peterborough, New Hampshire, she passes a sign that piques her curiosity: The McDowell Colony. Lucy turns at the sign and follows the road to a charming white house, and when she realizes she has stumbled upon an artist colony, she asks for a job application. After several interviews, she lands a job at the front desk. In her new environment, Lucy lives in a state of fascination, learns quickly, and meets people who love what she loves: writing, art, film, music. Lucy thrives, grows her craft, and eventually writes some clever, meaningful poetry that gets published in *The Sun* magazine.

Here we witness the Great Mystery in action. How does it work? I don't know. But I do know that God's Universal Ears perk up when somebody passionately asks for something that matches their purpose in life. Lucy's yearning was her asking, and it was loaded with passion and authenticity. It was a form of prayer that signaled benevolent forces to step forward and escort her toward her new life. (They probably sat in the passenger seat and whispered directions to Peterborough.) And what about faith and Lucy's inner knowing? We saw both as she hopped in that car and drove toward something better.

Of course, we never expect help to arrive in the form of a hurricane, but sometimes that's what it takes to shove us out the door. But as long as we hunger for our dreams and remain open to cosmic intervention, we can trust that even miserable circumstances can lead us to unimaginable joys. It helps to know that.

Because my *thoughts* have caused a great deal of suffering in my life, I make an effort to commune with Spirit. I am not talking about begging God or some outer force to eliminate headaches, rather, for insight. Directions. Being in the flow of life allows me to recognize answers when they come and delivers that great antidote to the stress that causes headaches and other health issues—peace.

Larry Dossey, MD, did not start his career with the intention of promoting prayer in his medical practice. For him, the union of medical science and spirituality happened naturally.

In his book, *Healing Words*, he shares research, perspectives, and experiences that definitively "allows science and spirituality to stand side by side in a complementary way, neither trying to usurp or eliminate the other." Through his research, Dossey provides us with rich insight:

> "Experiments with people showed that prayer positively affected high blood pressure, wounds, heart attacks, headaches, and anxiety . . . Remarkably, the effects of prayer did not depend on whether the praying person was in the presence of the organism being prayed for, or whether he or she was far away; healing could take place either on site or at a distance. Nothing seemed capable of stopping or blocking prayer. Even when an 'object' was placed in a lead-lined room or in a cage that shielded it from all known forms of eletromagnetic energy, the effect still got through."

In *Healing Words*, Dossey clarifies he isn't "selling" prayer. However, he thinks the subject is neglected in the world of medical science and discusses it for patients "to do with as they wish."

As an adult, I needed to understand truth outside the narrow confines of my culture. I could not figure out how to follow my mother's directive to "just be yourself" because I was extremely guarded against criticism and judgment. As events unfolded in my life, I learned to tune in to the questions and answers that came from the voice within myself. The solutions were not always easy, and certainly not without pain, for myself and others.

When I moved to the Southwest, I had my mother's total support ("You go live your life, Sweetie!"), but I am still haunted by the worried look on her face as she waved goodbye from the front porch of our family home in Pensacola, Florida. The suffering of others always causes me pain, but the insights I sought were, indeed, waiting for me on that journey, and I was able to gradually understand the tension that had resided in me for so long.

Seven years in New Mexico and Colorado taught me the value of surrender and being in the present moment. They also expanded my knowledge of the power of thought and prayer. All I had to do was ask, and the Creator of the universe provided answers—in unexpected ways I call miracles.

As miracle after miracle appeared, I began to understand how past experiences, including hurtful events, were strung into a series of encounters that had moved me forward throughout my life. It was like following breadcrumbs on a long, educational trail. Every step on the path purified my inner world and expanded my capacity to love myself, stop judging others, and let go of restrictive fears. As the voice within grew ever-stronger, the line between inner and outer prayers grew thin.

Not everyone has to get divorced or worry their mother to grow. Not everyone needs to go on a physical journey to heal. That's *my* story; it's what *I* had to do. I needed distance to find objectivity. The Southwestern culture and geography provided perspectives crucial to my development and my healing. But someone else's growth chart might look entirely different. My road map may say "turn left," while yours says "turn right." Our divergent paths will create wildly divergent experiences and fascinating outcomes. It is comforting to know that no matter where we are, asking (prayer) followed by listening (waiting for insight), works.

In the end, my years in New Mexico and Colorado were one long prayer made of countless short prayers—some sent from mountaintops, others from my car, my office, the grocery store, my journal, exercise classes—anywhere and everywhere. Every act that quieted my mind connected me to my inner voice and the Creator. Maybe planting flowers is your prayer. Or feeding bread to seagulls. There are many ways to find guidance—to commune. Our lives, it seems, are living prayers, so however you choose to ask for answers, find a way to tune yourself to the "Receive" channel.

Ask for direction.

Then listen.

36

THE POWER OF
THE MIND & BODY

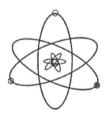

Yet only one thing must be remembered: There is no effect
without a cause and there is no lawlessness in creation.

Albert Einstein

Have you ever tripped in a dream and felt your sleeping body jerk? That's because the dreaming mind can't distinguish between literal and imagined reality—it's a mechanism that carries tremendous implications for healing.

Many direct experiences have shown me how perception and the mind operate the chemistry and responses of the physical body. This understanding is crucial for eliminating headaches. Susan Danahy, PhD, is a talented clinical psychologist from my headache therapy days who taught me how what we *think* we see causes physiological changes to the body and affects our behavior.

One person might see a blue blanket in a gift shop and think *What a beautiful blue blanket. I have to have it!* For her, the blue blanket carries positive associations, perhaps of being safe and warm, tucked in at bedtime. Another person might see the same blanket and feel nauseated—*Blue blanket! Yipes! Let me out of here!* Maybe it reminds him of a scary experience, like being tangled up in a blue blanket. Our perceptions turn out to be a collection of how-to lessons from past experiences and a long scroll of rules developed by our culture, geography, and groups: family, neighborhood, church, school, and more.

A simplified explanation of the synergy of mind and body goes something like this: First, one observes an event. The event is internally labeled and judged based upon previous experiences and beliefs. Next, one draws a conclusion which results in an action.

Of course, when we look closely, we see that our personal beliefs about people, places, and things are not the only reality. My version of an experience is just *my story* about it. If I make room for others to have their own, different, stories about the same experience, I find relief and eliminate the need to be "right" or control others. Letting go of the need to be right replaces headache-producing anger with calm observation. Understanding the mind-body process also encourages us to expand our capacity for compassion while promoting peaceful thinking and body chemistry that dethrones headaches.

Once we become aware of our pre-recorded mindsets, we can lighten up, laugh at ourselves, and make better decisions because our minds have escaped from their cages. We can stop judging and enjoy life without trying to manipulate it. Such liberty is a contagious freedom fighter for people with headaches.

Traffic intolerance (road rage) used to be one of my less attractive habits. If a driver cut me off, then slowed to twenty miles an hour in a thirty-five mile an hour zone, resentment would zing my body with the chemicals of anger. I would think, *Idiot! What a macaroon!* It did not take long to realize that every time I became angry, I got a headache. My only option was to drop my self-importance and reframe my thinking: *Everyone else has a right to the road, too,* or *That could be my grandmother driving that car.* It took work to replace reactivity with calmness, but it was worth it.

At one juncture of my life, I worked for the New Mexico Supreme Court, introducing new computer software to court system employees sprinkled across New Mexico. I was miserable in the job because the software bombed-out every twenty minutes, punctuating my days with classrooms of students glaring at me as if I were single-handedly ruining their lives.

I felt like a yutz and grew angry with myself for being associated with such a substandard product. These indigestible feelings were amplified by an associate (I'll call her "Maurie") who was a bonafide control freak of a woman with a penchant for metaphorically throwing me under the bus. I avoided her as much as possible, but even so, she was the source of a lot of misery—and headaches. The situation worsened when I had to travel to Arizona with her for a training. Oh, boy. Red-alert.

By the end of our first day of instruction, I felt so stressed that my head was screaming. I nonetheless agreed to visit a shopping mall with Maurie. Once we were there, I finagled some time alone in a department store where I became enthralled with a perfect-fit moss green skirt and blouse—so enthralled that by the time I walked away from the cashier, the headache was gone. Totally gone. *Astonishingly* gone.

Hmmmm. I wondered, *What happened there?* I knew the answer: my mind had been laser-focused on something pleasant that changed my body chemistry, which eliminated the headache.

An extraordinary lesson in the power of the mind also presented itself when I volunteered to paint canvas banners for *The Shakespeare in Santa Fe* festival at St. John's College.

Upon entering the college's art studio, I found seven un-stretched canvases lying across large tables. Each canvas measured about 3' wide and 6' long and bore the penciled outline of a Renaissance image, like a coat-of-arms, crossed swords, or other medieval elements. I selected the canvas depicting the bust and face of a Renaissance maiden. "Crimson" had been written on the maiden's cheek, "blue" indicated the color of her irises, and so on. As other artists drifted into the room, I prepared my paints and began to brush color onto my canvas.

An hour and a half into the process, the artist who designed the canvases unexpectedly burst through the door with a friend. It was an entrance befitting a king. Brushes were abandoned, hands went to cheeks.

The man was tall, red-faced, and loud, with a presence that overtook the room. His friend launched into a fast, high pitched summation of the gathering: "Oh, Reggie! It's like you're *Michelangelo,* and these" (waving a hand our way), "are your *apprentices!*"

I wanted to throw my brush at him.

The rest of the painters stopped and fawned over Reggie, who was clearly famous: "It was *soooo* good to see you at the gala! That installation was just *maah-vah-lous* . . ." I felt my physiology ramp up its output of agitated chemicals. When the initial glorification ended, Reggie was introduced to us unknowns. I was introduced last, clearly an afterthought. As a courtesy, I managed a weird circular wave that served as my hello and continued to paint from my silent position by the windows.

On the outside, I'm sure I looked like a woman bent to her task, but I was fuming. After painting the maiden's face, I worked on the bodice of her dress. Stroke after stroke, I painted while listening to the continued aggrandizement of the artist. The falsetto voices and every overdone word threw fuel on my internal storm of brewing, toxic emotions, but I remained silent, and kept painting.

When it was time to paint the border of the canvas, I ran into trouble when I could not mix a vibrant shade of purple. I had just begun my fourth attempt to create the elusive color when I noticed something odd about my blood. It was boiling. In my veins. I could feel it. Literally. An expression of my mother's sprung to mind: "I was so mad it made my blood boil;" I was shocked to discover that it described a real, physical phenomenon.

So there I was with boiling blood and crummy purple paint on my palette—the bubbling blood the result of my dislike (massive understatement) for the artist—when one random, compassionate thought dropped into my mind: *Hey, wait a minute! Why is this man like this?* (loud, egotistical) and the answer came immediately. *Because he doesn't feel good about himself.* Two other kind thoughts followed: *His sycophantic friend feels even worse and is trying to feel better by association with Reggie,* and *these other people are trying to feel good by rubbing shoulders with both Reggie and his companion!* And with this kind-hearted clarity, a strange tingling sensation immediately presented itself on the bottoms of my feet and began to march steadily upward.

An energy akin to sparks from a sparkler traveled from my feet into my ankles, then moved upward toward my calves. After passing through my knees, it rose into my thighs, hips, mid-section. I stood frozen, a living statue holding a paintbrush, observing the curious wave as it rippled through my ribs toward my chest. At this point, I was worried. *Am I having a heart attack? Is this a heart attack? Because if it is, it's not bad.* With a surreal sense of observation, I felt the tingling climb as it approached my heart, and then swept through my chest and shoulders. *Still alive.* It continued into my neck and throat (*still alive*), then passed out through the top of my head. And *ka-poof!* within that brief span of sixty seconds, I was full, like a water pitcher that had been filled with clear sparkling water, except I was brimming with love. That's the most accurate way I can describe the experience. It was stunning.

In this rarified condition, I stared at my failed purple paint, and heard my voice, as if disembodied, say, "Reggie?" which is when the room of murmuring fans fell deadly silent. It was as if my vocalization contained powerful magic. When his name flew from my throat, it felt as if a ball of otherworldly contents had been launched, splashing the room as it flew. The love that filled me had announced itself through my voice. I know this because I was there. I heard it. The other painters heard it. Reggie heard it.

The next sound was Reggie's voice piercing the hushed room. "Yes, Elizabeth?" (I was surprised he knew my name.)

"I need your help." (Me, asking for help from a man I

had detested sixty seconds prior.)

Reggie came over, considered my canvas, mixed an exquisite color of purple for my border, then returned to his table. The room gradually resumed its hum.

Right before Reggie left, he walked over to me, commented on my canvas, shook my hand, and said, "I hope I'll see you again." Interestingly, I was the only one he visited before he walked out the door.

This psycho-emotional, physical transformation from hate to love was one of the most profound spiritual experiences of my life. It took only one pure thought to viscerally change the chemistry of hate (ego) burning in my veins into peace, love, goodwill, and health. The chain reaction of mental, chemical, and emotional impacts on my body, behavior, and the people around me, left me with an indelible mega-lesson that demanded further investigation.

Every illuminating experience I have teaches me more about the affects of the mind, and in my case, how very wrong I can be when my ego is running the show. Because self-awareness is invaluable to me, I work every day to foster a spirit of love and kindness that supports personal joy and extends to others. It's my attempt to save the world, save you (from me), and save myself.

There is a calm and beautiful, non-flummoxed being living beneath the ego, one that knows the answers—and *that* one does not have headaches.

REST

Rest is not idleness,
and to lie on the grass
under trees on a summer's day,
listening to the murmur of the water,
or watching the clouds float across the sky,
is by no means a waste of time.

John Lubbock

Rest and sleep are cousins. Sleep is the cousin that slides us from consciousness into the realm of slumber where our bodies and brains clean and regenerate themselves. Rest puts us into a state of wakeful repose. It's petting the cat, staring at the sea, or sitting on the porch listening to the rain—nowhere to go, nothing to do. Rest is important, and is as indispensable as sleep.

Thankfully, it's easy to build rest into our lives. Our success, though, depends on a commitment to punctuate our days with rest periods *no matter what*. The commitment is important because it puts an end to exhausting mental deliberations: *Should I go to the beach or mop the floor? Should I call George, Mary, and Minnie, or sit in the garden?* A resolution to participate in periods of rest is a pledge of allegiance to one's well-being.

Real rest is easier to accomplish without the presence of technology. When I need rest, I turn my cell phone OFF and put it where I am not tempted to turn it on. My phone doesn't work in the mountains, which is one reason I find the mountains restful. And I am secretly relieved when I accidentally leave my phone at home because aloneness transports me into a state of presence. I especially like the feeling of simply *being*, mouth shut, happy to observe the life around me.

You may want to make a list of activities you find restful, and schedule them throughout your week. I mean, literally, put them on the calendar. Feel free to spontaneously add more rest periods, but view these appointments as sacred—because they are. My list includes reading, taking a salt bath, sitting under my pecan trees, and lying on the grass. I also love to sit with a friend on the beach and gaze, wordlessly, at the water. Heaven. Essential.

#38

LETTING GO,
SYNCHRONICITY & MIRACLES

Think how it is to have a conversation with an embryo.
You might say, "The world outside is vast and intricate.
There are wheatfields and mountain passes,
and orchards in bloom.
At night there are millions of galaxies, and in sunlight
the beauty of friends dancing at a wedding."
You ask the embryo why he, or she, stays cooped up
in the dark with eyes closed.
Listen to the answer.

Rumi

Life sometimes presents us with scary circumstances. Situations. It's easy to brace against worrisome conditions and tense up for fear of making a "mistake." We might turn the wrong way, say the wrong thing, choose the wrong job, husband, wife, city, car, life. Such worry, however, only muddles our performance and exacerbates headaches. Enter the superhero in our story: the inner voice—the gallant vehicle that will drive us anywhere we want to go. If we trust it and follow its directions, that interior wisdom will take us to a world of delightful, synchronistic experiences.

Fear caused me to ignore my inner voice. I held on to people, places, and things when I should have let them go. After I learned to follow the *voice*, I was able to benefit from the zigzags I encountered in my life. Instead of ignoring my fear, I walked through it. Once I let go of control, my life opened up. Eventually, I allowed events to play their intended roles. My brother Anson's death hurt so badly I couldn't bear to sit still, so I left Pensacola and moved to New Mexico and Colorado. Without my Southwest experiences, I would not have the insights that helped me heal and write this book. Though the journey was harsh, it eventually returned me to an authentic life. The truth is if I had listened to my inner voice as a child and teenager, I would never have walked into the situations that caused the headaches in the first place.

I once stored my possessions in a warehouse. Family furniture, artwork, dolls, toys, books from my childhood—everything sat in the dark for seven years. I was exhilarated when I retrieved these belongings and put them in my new home, but very quickly, the sheer quantity of those objects started to suffocate me. I realized I needed to clear some things out, get a fresh start, but I was frozen with indecision: *How can I possibly part with the vase Mary gave me? What if I regret getting rid of this cool dress? It's from my first dance!* I was paralyzed with indecision.

My friend, Eileen, came to the rescue by helping me start the clearing process. We started with my clothes. By the time Eileen was finished with me, the thrift store had five bags of clothing, and I had a very bare closet plus a noticeably lighter emotional and mental attitude. I felt so good that I cleared out other unnecessary items—shoes, sheets, funky water pitchers. Clearing out possessions quenched my thirst for space and freedom and moved me closer to my unencumbered dream life. (I still have too much "stuff.")

Another friend, Patty, once told me a story about a little girl who received a pop-bead "pearl" necklace for Christmas. The child loved the necklace so much she clutched her plastic beads in her hands even in her sleep. Seeing how much she loved her fake pearls, her father decided to buy her *real* pearls. But there was a problem—the little girl refused to let go of her pop-beads.

"Trust me," the father said, but the little girl could not let go of the cheap necklace—could not allow her hands to be empty. Moral of the story: new and unexpected surprises can only come to us when we make room for them.

Of course, there are many ways to let go. When people die, we *have* to let go—sooner or later. When we buy a new car, we generally hand over the old one. We lose friends, then make new ones. Lifestyles can change due to divorce, lost jobs, or moving from one state to another, but every loss contains gain and opportunity for growth. Whenever my mother and I went to an antique show, we would *ooh* and *ahh* over heirloom items, especially beautiful jewelry. But when we walked away from a tempting necklace or ring, my mother would remind me, "There will always be beautiful things." I had a wise mother.

You have probably witnessed the recent popularity of books and programs dedicated to creating clutter-free lives. Organizing consultant Marie Kondo gained celebrity teaching people to simplify spaces (and life) by letting go of unnecessary goods. Her methods are found in books like *Spark Joy, An Illustrated Master Class on the Art of Organizing and Tidying Up*. There are countless space clearing books and videos to inspire and demonstrate the benefits of space-clearing. Check them out; you may find one that motivates you to lighten your load.

Clearing the past makes way for the new—new relationships, new possibilities, and miracles. I have come to embrace the unknown and find it invigorating because stepping into the unfamiliar results in exhilarating interactions, clarity, and expanded options. Even when new territory leads to unpleasant places, the lessons learned can be more valuable than the crown jewels—if one has eyes to see them. This was the case when I entered into a relationship with "Blake."

Blake broke my heart when I was twenty-six. When I was forty-eight, I cleaned out a box and found the only love note he ever wrote to me. As I read it, I realized the letter wasn't about his love for me at all. How could I have been so mistaken? In reality, I had allowed myself to be mistreated throughout the relationship. I reread the letter, shaking my head, wondering *Why have I kept this thing for so long?* As I dropped it into a trash can, I had one thought: *Goodbye!* Goodbye to the past. Goodbye to bad habits. Goodbye to pretending.

But wait.

Within a month of tossing the letter, Blake called—after *twenty-two years*. Clearly, he had sensed my disconnection when I threw away his letter. (How else can one explain it? Coincidence? I think not.) Blake wanted to see me. He said he'd always loved me. (I'm sure you can see this one coming, but at the time, I shut off my voice of wisdom, and put on my blinders.)

After months of long-distance conversations, Blake asked if I would come visit him. Uh-oh. I was slipping. I really *wanted* to believe in prince charming fairy tales. Because I was impulsive during that period of my life, I lost my bearings. The prince and I discussed marriage, and with his assurances, I gave away most of my possessions (including a piano) and moved to Kentucky.

The lure of a fairytale healing of the old relationship had snagged me. *See? He loved me all along. I am worth something. Ain't it great? Isn't life amazing?* (Forget discernment, insert skipping through fields of clover.) Things were all yip, yay, and yahoo on the surface, but my inner voice was screaming *Nooo!* before I even boarded the plane. Despite the sense I was in for a rough ride, I buckled my seatbelt and took the flight to relationship fantasyland.

It didn't take long to realize the relationship was another "educational" experience. By then, I was firmly ensconced in a situation rife with big accusations over little things. Everything I did was wrong, and I found myself tiptoeing around. That's when an uprising of headaches stormed the walls in an attempt to reiterate the clear message to get out of the house, but my tenacity and a finely-honed ability to deceive myself kept me fighting to stay—I thought I could change the course of things.

The demolition of the relationship took nine months. By the time I moved into an apartment, I was distraught, emotionally battered, had few possessions, and a skull-splitting headache. I really needed to talk to someone, so I pressed my hand against my aching head and dialed my cousin, Lesley.

During our conversation, she said, "It's interesting that you called because someone asked about you the other day—they had a job for you."

"Really?" I lowered my headache-pressing hand.

"Yes. He had a job working with kids, and he wondered if you were around."

Two tick-tock seconds passed before I said, "Give me his number."

Within three weeks, I was driving cross-country toward a wonderful new job in Colorado with another notch on my miracle bedpost.

While the first part of the tale of my moving from Santa Fe to Kentucky appears to be a horror story, in retrospect, it was a cosmically clever way to dynamite me out of a bad-habit rut. After the relationship collapsed, I told every friend who would listen about how unfairly, disrespectfully, and wrongly I'd been treated. In time, I revisited the dirt pile of bad memories, only to find a big old diamond in the trash heap—a bright lesson from the inner voice: *You heard yourself say no, but you walked in anyway. Now, do you get it? Can we move on now?*

The whispered inner message to call my cousin was part of a dance that happens when I am quiet and aligned with the Divine. Whatever your beliefs, you can imagine how grateful I was to have heard and responded to the inner calling. Not only did I return to my beloved Colorado, but my new job landed me in my favorite profession.

It took years, but I gradually learned to relinquish control and judgment, trusting that whenever I found myself standing in the shadows empty-handed, something greater was working on my behalf. Eventually, letting go became second nature—central to disarming headaches.

The times I hear and *follow* the inner voice, I am rewarded with experiences that are full of peace—sometimes, awe. The following story offers an example of the benefits I experience when I follow my sense of knowing. Perhaps you can relate it to your journey.

One of the most blissful nights of my life occurred during my journey West. Before I left on the trip, my mother had repeatedly encouraged me: "You live your life the way you want to, Sweetie," and after I took the leap into the unknown, I discovered the refreshing feeling of being in compliance with myself, and *only* myself. While I still struggled with headaches, each turn of my jeep's wheels brought me expanded views of my life.

When my travels took me to the high desert of Taos, New Mexico, I stumbled upon an interesting building—*The Abominable Snow Mansion*. My curiosity demanded a look inside where I was greeted by a handsome young man named Doan, who explained that *The Abominable Snow Mansion* was an inn and a hostel. The large living room featured a piano, sofas, chairs, and a pool table. I signed up for a bunk, and by afternoon I was invited to accompany Doan and a group of strangers to the hot springs located at the bottom of the Taos Gorge. There were rules: we had to start at midnight, and no flashlights were allowed. Such adventures were new to me, so I consulted my intuition to ascertain the veracity of my new friends. The answer was *Yes!* to the trek down the gorge, despite a moderate headache.

That is how I came, at 11:30 on a clear, star-filled night, to be in the back seat of a stranger's truck zooming along the edge of the Taos Gorge with five unknown people, my hair blowing out of the window. Enraptured, I stuck out a cosmic whisker in the direction of my mother: *I'm doing it, Mom! I'm really living my life.* We parked at the top of the canyon and began our cautious hike down.

The path was narrow, carved by wear into the gorge's steep walls, and our group traveled single file until we reached the canyon floor. Once on the bottom, we stepped out of our bathing suits and into our choice of natural hot-water pools. Actually, everyone stepped out of their bathing suits except for two modest Southern girls—Susan from Texas, and me—and Doan, who wore his briefs out of consideration for his more Puritan companions. Each of us lay back, gazing at a ceiling of stars glittering above the gorge. As the hot springs warmed us, the Rio Grande rustled by; crisp night air cleansed our lungs. Eventually, a full moon peeked over the top edge of the gorge; we watched as it slowly crossed overhead, then hiked back up the trail before the remaining moonlight fell behind the opposite side of the gorge. Warm water, cool air, and fascination with the new and marvelous—how could a headache survive that much wonder and joy? It didn't—in spite of the high altitude.

I thank synchronicity for that experience—God, The Universe, The Creator—all the names that apply to that beautiful Spirit that arranges holy events and gives us the courage to accept them. My headaches had been trying to tell me something—many things—for years. As I learned to listen and practiced letting go, life rewarded me.

All I wanted was more.

The word "miracles" puts a lot of people on standby. It's a bold word. I use it when referring to events that reach beyond the realm of superficiality—circumstances that bear the mark of something greater intervening in my life. Miracles can't be manufactured, and until experienced, there can be room for doubt. But once one miracle manifests itself, it becomes easier to recognize the next one and the next one until miracles tie the reality of one's life together like knots in lacework.

Miracles are sometimes called "coincidences"—a person you meet in a grocery store line says three words that throw light onto an emotional issue that has begged for your attention. And standing there, tomatoes in-hand, an insight floats into your mind. No matter what you call such moments or your specific beliefs, openness and awareness lead to marvelous phenomena that foster a yearning for understanding of what I call The Great Mystery. My desire for knowledge has led me to see that miracles do indeed happen in our universe. An example is the time my two teenage brothers went on an adventure in a small boat with two friends: Marvin and Dudley.

The excursion took the boys to a pond in the woods. Marvin was sporting a new, gold, high-school ring that his hardworking parents had just given him. During the fun, the cherished ring slipped from his finger into the murky water.

The four boys dove ceaselessly, scouring the muddy bottom with their hands. The more they searched, the muddier the water became until it was like brown soup. Twilight was turning toward night when the dejected boys gave up the search. But my brother, Edgar, hung onto the side of the boat and said a short prayer, "Please, God . . ." then dove into the murkiness one final time—which is when the ring slipped onto his finger.

The first time I heard this story, I felt such amazement and was so star-struck by the power of my brother's absolute sweetness, I couldn't say a word. I was silenced by his ability to align himself with God, the Great Benevolent Presence (however you reference the Great Mystery). This type of experience increased my desire to understand how we, as individuals, participate in the God connection. I was fascinated by the unfathomable complexity that resides in our brains and bodies. How do we understand truths that aren't available to our conscious, intellectually-oriented minds? In itself, that reality is a miracle. Regardless of how we connect, openness is key.

My first mind-boggling experience with the communion of all things came in the arms of a mimosa tree. As a child, I often wedged myself into one of the tree's smooth Y-shaped branches where I sat and wrote poetry. I had been writing for a while one day when a soft breeze floated across my skin. Something about the quality of the gentle wind seemed to carry a message. I tucked my yellow pencil into my book and looked up into a clear blue sky dotted by fragrant pink mimosa blossoms. The sun warmed me, leaves swayed, and suddenly everything in the universe came together as one thing. For those few moments, I was a part of all creation, and everything made sense. I sat transfixed by the sensation until the spell wore off.

The mimosa tree encounter instilled a strong belief in the connectivity of all things, and later, when headaches came to call, it gave me confidence that there was a solution to my struggle with pain. I was fortunate to be raised in an atmosphere that fostered awareness, but it still took time, effort, and energy to heal.

If I could do it, you can do it.

Colorado is one of the places I go to heal, connect, and find clarity. The silence of snow, grandeur of mountains, and vast expanses of land clear my mind and reunite me with my emotions, creativity, and heart. One powerful healing phase occurred in the late 1990s.

One day, I felt a pressing need to hike even though the weather was I-could-kill-you cold. Conditions were so bad there was only one other car in the parking lot at the trailhead, but I hopped out anyway and began to walk the surface of a frozen river.

After a short distance, I realized the air was too frigid to breathe, and I decided to go home. But as I turned to go back, I caught sight of a woman walking toward me on the ice. I waved, then waited until she reached me, and we chatted as we walked back to our cars.

"What do you do?" I asked, and as if on cue, she told me she taught a class to free people from the emotional wounds inflicted by trauma, and, big surprise, her specialty matched my form of trauma. Magic.

I took the woman's class, which led to several major healing events, one of which was telling my mother about the experience that had locked me down when I was nineteen— the nightmare that had initiated the headaches. When I finished my story, my mother embraced me and said, "Oh, Sweetie! I always thought something must have happened." There we stood, mother and daughter, crying together. Her love let me sob out the sorrow, hurt, and shame that had been locked away for decades. Such is the healing power of sharing the truth, especially with a loving mother.

I find the sequence of events in this story remarkable. The healing gift of unburdening myself with my mother started with an inner urge that led me to a frozen river where I met the perfect person to assist in my healing process. I had been given another, loving, mystical setup—synchronicity at its finest; another chunk of the headache web had been demolished.

Letting go, synchronicity, and miracles have been vital to my recovery from headaches. To further illustrate the power of synchrony, I offer the story of Amma. It is one of my favorite illustrative miracle stories.

The first time someone told me they were going to "sit" with Mata Amritanadamayi, "Amma" for short, I asked, "What does 'sitting' mean?" My more evolved friends patiently explained, but I still didn't understand.

Amma was a holy woman who had prayed so ceaselessly as a child that local townspeople thought she was crazy. In reality, Amma's calling was to travel the world praying, hugging people, and modeling love. She became an emissary for goodness, blessing people like me, and participating in global peace works such as delivering the keynote address at the United Nations' first Academic Impact Conference on Technology and Sustainable Development. In 2014, *The Huffington Post* selected her as one of the fifty most powerful female religious leaders in the world. Amma has collaborated with the pope (Pope Francis). Hundreds of thousands of people travel to sit in Amma's presence, most of them searching for the opportunity to be hugged and blessed by the holy woman.

As my spirituality evolved, so did my desire to meet Amma. I had not yet accomplished my wish when I dispensed with my possessions and prepared to leave the Southwest to return to Florida because my elderly mother needed me. On the way, I stopped in Santa Fe to visit with friends, one of whom, "Megan," had just moved to Los Angeles. Megan suggested I fly out to see her and meet her boyfriend before moving to Florida. Before we hung up the phone, she said, "Oh, and Amma will be here! Greg and I have already seen her, but we'll go again—with you." At last, synchronicity was lining things up so I could see Amma. I was delighted.

Megan met me at the airport and drove me to her apartment where I met her boyfriend, whose lack of fondness for me became immediately evident. (I was so uncomfortable there I ended up in a Los Angeles ER with a horrific headache.) The night before my return to Santa Fe, the three of us went to see Amma, even though Megan and Greg had received Amma's blessing two days prior. Forty-five minutes before my turn to be blessed by the holy woman (I had waited three hours), Greg said, "You know, I think I'll go home." I was shocked when Megan said, "Me, too." It was three o'clock in the morning. I was in an unfamiliar city with no vehicle, so I had little alternative but to leave with them—without my blessing from the holy woman.

I was still in a disappointed funk when I boarded a plane to Santa Fe the next morning. During a layover in Denver, I passed the time by calling my friend, Anne, from the airport. "What time will you make it back to Santa Fe?" she asked. "Amma's here, and we could go see her."

I said, "*What?* Amma was in Los Angeles last night!"

"Well, she's in Santa Fe now."

I laughed out loud and said, "Great. I'll call you when I land in Albuquerque."

How about that? Another miracle!

However . . .

Bad weather left me stranded in Denver for five hours, and by the time I talked with Anne again, she had already been to see Amma, reporting she had left the ashram around 7:00 p.m. where "things were winding down."

Aargh! Missed again. What a yo-yo ride of emotions. *Was there something so wrong with me that I wasn't being allowed to see Amma?*

My flight finally landed in Albuquerque at 11:00 p.m. I was leaning against a post, waiting for an airport bus to Santa Fe when a young man walked over and said, "Are you going to an ashram?"

"Why are you asking me that?"

"I don't know," he said, and continued to stand in front of me.

"Are you talking about Amma?"

He nodded. "Yes."

Kaboom! My spirit skyrocketed.

I called another friend, Sheri, in Santa Fe. Sheri met our bus at the Santa Fe airport then loaned me her car so my new friend and I could hoof it over to the ashram. Hopeful, we slipped out of our shoes and hurried into a cozy room where we found Amma beaming from a small stage. About forty fellow seekers sat on the floor, absorbed in music, witnessing the blessings Amma gave to each participant—including me. Joy!

The perfect time and place to be blessed by the holy woman had been waiting for me all along—what a fun, cosmic joke. I was humbled to receive Amma's blessing in a warm, intimate setting and tickled about the journey required to get there.

The moral of the story is to keep going and believe in life's possibilities. Amazing solutions are concocted behind the scenes. When the tableau looks bleak, take a breath.

Let go.

Continue.

Believe.

One final story about synchronicity and miracles . . .

I was shopping for eyeglasses in New Orleans when a young woman and I started consulting with each other: "Now *those* are a definite *no* . . . try these." A quiet look in the mirror, back to the young woman. "Ooooh. Those are *cute!*" And we went on like that for half an hour until I asked her what she did for a living.

"I'm a student at Tulane."

"What are you studying?"

"Neuro-medicine."

A familiar tingle that had come to signal miracles sprang to life as we began a conversation about headaches and issues surrounding conventional and alternative medicine.

I said, "If you go into the treatment of headaches, I hope you include holistic methods in your approach. It's hard to find a medical doctor who looks at core causes—the whole person. Mainly, neurologists prescribe drugs, but when I had headaches, I needed someone who would look deeper—see the total picture."

She listened, then asked a few questions.

I told her about being hospitalized—about the long years and experiences it took for me to find my way out of the maze created by headaches.

"You need to do a TED talk," she said.

"Seriously?"

"Definitely. I think anyone who has something to say needs to say it."

Oh, boy.

I looked at her. A moment of silence passed.

"And Tulane funds talks like yours, and I am the head of the student organization for neuro-medicine for Tulane. You should talk to Tulane."

She gave me her name, I bought my glasses, said "Bye now," and walked down Magazine Street grateful for our synchronistic meeting. That encounter in an eyeglass store led me to the idea of creating a TED talk, which amplified my desire to write the book you hold in your hands.

After years of observing the progression of life's events, I have come to see how synchronicity happens all the time. Now, whenever things seem off, I know I'm either not listening or not seeing the whole picture.

I have learned to let go and trust that the great Creator and a specialized group of Cosmic Operations Managers hear me. I can't explain how it works, but I have learned to hear and heed their whispered directions and get out of the way. When I get quiet, let go of the reins, and listen to my inner voice, I am escorted to Something Greater. My habit of looking backwards at old injuries has slowly been replaced by open anticipation of wonders current and yet to come. My personal observations have convinced me that everyone has a band of angels, and as musician James Taylor sings in "Country Road," *They're comin' to set me free.*

Guess what? They're comin' for you, too.

#39

FRIENDS

It is one of the blessings of old friends
that you can afford to be stupid with them.

Ralph Waldo Emerson

The book, *Unlikely Friendships,* by Jennifer Holland, holds top position on my coffee table. It's a volume crammed with photographs and true stories of animals with unusual friends—a leopard and a Brahman cow, a greyhound and a long-eared owl, a poodle and a nearsighted deer (they sleep in a bed together). All of the stories highlight the extra-special bond found in real friendships.

Many people appear in our lives. Each plays a role, as if in a theatrical production—someone plays the bad guy, someone else the fool. A character enters stage left, plays her part, then exits stage right, never to be seen again. Some players never leave the stage. While all characters in the stories of our lives are important, some are crucial—like true friends—and that's especially valid for people who have headaches.

True friends are the dependable people who know everything about us and stick around anyway. They care about us, and we can count on them whether the chips are up or down—whether the headaches are dead or alive.

Friends support us in many ways. They bring us a sense of family. Sometimes they *are* family. They give us support (time, help, presence, hugs, laughter, vegetable soup) and stability. They answer their phones when we call, stand beside us at funerals, and when we fall, they catch us before we hit the ground. Good friends are the people who cheerlead our dreams and help us find a way to fulfill them, all of which chases headaches out of our lives.

The *opposite* of healthy friends are the people who freak out, blame, or accuse us when we lay our souls bare. Allies exhibit uplifting traits like honesty, kindness, loyalty, and thoughtfulness. We want to interact with people who strengthen and make us better people—people who won't let us get away with our own baloney but won't hammer us over the head with it, either. We want friends who can talk through anything, including trouble in the friendship, and come out with an even stronger alliance.

I don't need the Mayo Clinic to tell me how important my friends are, but it's nice to know that international scientists have researched the subject and consistently link a strong social network to good health. They tell us that having friends reduces health problems like depression, high blood pressure, and other symptoms related to headaches. I know what happens to me when I don't see my friends—it's not pretty.

Real friends are allowed to enter the holy ground of my soul because I trust them; they are *for* me. My friends aren't perfect, but they bear admirable characteristics—or at least, aspire to them. They care when I'm sick and hold me when I cry. When I wrestle with scary life circumstances and sift through painful facts, my friends stand with me. They offer ideas and consolation that help me replace the debris of my past with the joy of today and a vision of a bright future—and we all know how that process expels the drudge of headaches.

My best friend, Deb, and I have become sister life-guides. We have built our relationship over eighteen years of laughing at ourselves, studying cosmic matters, watching funny movies (*Shrek*), losses, and working through issues. She has born my personality chinks with elegance. I have driven her crazy with my intensity and habit of using "too many words!" I have been angry with her a maximum of four times, and we have worked through every wound with grace, honesty, and love. Deb and I drop our guards when we are together, and we can say anything to each other because we have mastered the honest communication techniques required by love, trust, and respect. The freedom to relax with a trusted friend like Deb has been elemental to releasing mental and physical tension that exacerbated my headaches. When I steer off course, she helps me recalibrate my mind. I try to do the same for her. That's the way true friendship works—in syncopated reciprocity. It's a clever dance—part tango, part jig.

I marvel at my many friends who love me with astounding loyalty and wildly generous hearts. How did I get these extraordinary friends? It took time, awareness, and work. Some of them were God-given. As I grew and learned to be honest with myself, I drifted away from friends who weren't a good fit. The shift usually happened naturally, but sometimes, leaving a friendship was intentional and painful. I didn't want to hurt anyone, but eventually, I didn't want to hurt *myself*. My friends also helped me recognize the need for self-care. After I learned to include myself in the friendship equation, I made great strides in leaving headaches behind.

Find friends, *real* friends who show up for you—people who rejoice when you do your happy dance.

#40

GRATITUDE

If the only prayer you ever say in your
entire life is thank you, it will be enough.

Meister Eckhart

Gratitude is one of the easiest ways to create good health because the mind that contemplates thankfulness generates the biochemistry of peace. We are talking about the kind of gratitude that views life as a gift—all of it. Gratefulness is a formidable way to shift negativity and create a personal biosphere of harmony that wards off headaches.

Years of beauty sprinkled with losses, followed by years of losses sprinkled with beauty, led me to gratitude and the ability to find it in unexpected places. I was raised in beauty, and when I was married, privileged to live with fine clothes, travel, and a beautiful home with lovely views of Pensacola Bay. I appreciated having a strong, healthy body, my family, good friends, and two cats, but I understood little of how it would be to live without them.

My brother, Anson, was naturally grateful for simple things. Of course, I was accustomed to rubbing shoulders with his inherent sweetness and quiet gratitude, but one day a modest lunch changed my life.

There was nothing unusual about Anson coming over— he was a regular at my house, and we had shared many meals together. On this particular day, he was sitting at my dining room table overlooking the bay when I served him a humble pimento cheese sandwich. As I put the plate on the table, he said, "Thank you, Elizabeth," with his trademark gentle sincerity. But this time, I was especially struck by the way his face glowed with appreciation. Glowed. Over a pimento cheese sandwich. I thought, *I want to be that grateful!* And I meant it, although, I had no idea how much that request would change my life.

Where did my wish take me? It took me to places of agonizing loss (including Anson), poverty, and heavy doses of loneliness. But I had asked for gratitude and, by George, I got it. I knew that my request for genuine gratitude had been fulfilled the afternoon a stranger invited me to her home and served me a cup of hot tea. I was so grateful, I cried.

In a stunning example of accentuating the positive, Joe, a lifetime friend, called me one lazy summer afternoon to deliver some news.

"Hey, Liz. How are you?"

"I'm good, buddy. How are you doing?"

"Well, I'm fine. I'm really good, but I need to tell you something." Joe paused. "Now before I tell you this . . ."

Another pause. "Everything's okay." And right there, I knew everything was *not* okay. "I'm in the hospital at the moment."

"What? In the *hospital!* For what? What's going on?"

"They had to take off my foot."

I was struck dumb. (It doesn't take much of an imagination to see the impact of losing a foot.) When I finished fumbling for words, Joe said, "I think about it this way . . . there are a lot of people in the world living productive lives without a foot. So it's okay. I'm alive." He said these words as casually as if he were ordering popcorn at a movie theatre—and he meant them. Wow. That interaction stuck with me.

Joe is a genuine teacher of gratitude.

Gratitude is a bit tricky to define. Is it a virtue? A behavior? An emotion? A prayer? Despite the vague nature of its definition, research has figured out a few things about its impact. Studies show that gratitude letters, journals, and lists promote happiness and benefit people who have medical and psychological challenges. Counselors often see noticeable improvement in the mental states of their clients when talk therapy incorporates gratitude exercises. Grateful cardiac patients enjoy better sleep and reduced cellular inflammation—the same type of inflammation that fosters headaches. Research has also found that grateful people are more resilient after traumatic events and experience less depression—an advantage every headache sufferer can appreciate.

One mental health study discovered that gratitude letters and lists that use fewer *negative* emotion words are key.

Success is not just about the addition of positive thinking and language, but includes a reduced focus on toxic emotions and events. Instead of ruminating on our negative experiences, gratitude helps us shift into a more constructive state. Remember, the mind changes the biochemistry of the brain and body.

Because gratitude lists are effective in generating positive mental states, I make a habit of writing them. Here's a sample of one of my abbreviated gratitude lists (notice the use of positive language). "Thank you for" is implied before each item on the list:

My good eyesight.

My strong, healthy body.

My good mind.

My talents.

My parents and family.

My friends.

The beauty of the Earth.

My beautiful home.

My good car.

Love, money, guidance.

Jason, for helping me with my computers.

Storms, rolling thunder, lightning, rain.

Birds singing.

My ears that allow me to *hear* birds sing.

My ability to see beauty.

People who teach me how to be a better, happier person.

My life.

The ability to hear and trust God.

The people who trust me.

You get the idea. Even a short, simple gratitude list can

shift perspectives, promote overall good health, and release headaches.

Gratitude has a funny way of compounding good things in my life. When I focus on gratitude for my healthy eyes, my overall health improves. When I express gratitude for my loving friends, they get more loving. This relationship between expressing appreciation and attracting positive elements into my life is real, and research supports my direct experience. The more I practice, the deeper the gratitude becomes, and the results build up over time—they last. I become healthier. Happier.

Even if you have to fake it at first, think grateful thoughts. Search every situation for its silver lining. Sift through the complaints, hurt, and resentments until you find thankfulness. Your family, friends, and co-workers will thank you. Your inflamed body will thank you. Soon, happiness will benefit your mental and physical states and help you forget you ever had headaches—and that's an event that skyrockets gratitude into a new and beautiful stratosphere.

#41

GOD & LOVE

Gravity explains the motions of the planets,
but it cannot explain who sets the planets in motion.
In the absence of any other proof,
the thumb alone would convince me of God's existence.

Isaac Newton

The search for communion with a divine presence is a treasure hunt loaded with gold nuggets for those who are intent on finding them. Thankfully, humans are imbued with a yearning to grow and the ability to co-create with the unexplainable spirit of grace that supports our lives. As we learn to use the equipment of being human, we discover endless potentialities and possibilities.

I've asked myself if I could have evolved without headaches. It's the kind of question people ask when they are in search of something more. Headaches certainly forced me to my spiritual knees. I would have done anything to solve the headache-hell problem earlier, but had it not been headaches, I suspect some other malady would have forced my hand—and my spiritual growth. So the answer is, I think so, and I don't know.

My awareness of the connectivity of all things has always served me. It has expanded through every experience of my life. It grows in sweat lodges, churches, personal therapy, and the bounty of nature. It reveals itself in artistic endeavors, meditation, and physical work. I find growth opportunities everywhere I go. I may climb a mountain on Wednesday, study metaphysics on Thursday, and go to church on Sunday.

My real life's work appears to be a spiritual affair, and the work required to live in the mystery has saved me. It held me up while I found my way out of a labyrinth of bad habits and erroneous beliefs that exacerbated head pain. It will hold you up, too. My way out of headaches involved phases: worn out, clueless, resting, exuberant, angry, broke, broken, hopeful, successful, enthusiastic. I could never have escaped the convoluted muddle without Divine intervention—whatever that means to you. I know what it means to me.

One example involves a rough patch that started in Arizona. I was continuously headachy, bone-tired, and low on money.

Santa Fe beckoned me, but I was so exhausted I couldn't move. I needed rest. Cue God, stage left, in the form of a conversation with a woman I met in a coffee shop. As the two of us shared stories of the road, I mentioned my dilemma. She said, "Why don't you stay in a monastery for a little while?"

"Monastery?" I tilted my head and looked at her like she was crazy. "I'm not Catholic."

"Doesn't matter."

I was astounded.

She told me about a monastery in Boulder, Colorado, and by afternoon Sister Margharita of the Abbey of St. Walburga, a silent order, had issued an open-armed invitation to stay.

It was twilight when I drove into the gravel parking lot. An atmosphere of serenity painted itself in a valley backed by the Rockies: quaint stone monastery, cows grazing in a green pasture, snow-capped violet mountains silhouetted by the sunset. Before I could get my car door open, Sister Margherita was walking out to greet me. I soon learned that she was the only nun allowed to talk—a necessity, it seemed, for serving people like me. Sister Margherita checked me in, handed me a schedule of the chapel services, and led me to a small room possessed of a twin bed, a straight-backed chair, and a chest of drawers. She suggested I rest a moment and told me she would return and lead me to dinner. *Dinner?* I was bedraggled, lost, and hungry—and deeply touched by her kindness. I put my clothes away and sat in the little chair until the sister returned and led me to the dining room.

I'm not sure how long I stood in the doorway staring at a buffet brimming with steaming foods before I looked around for the crowd that would eat such a banquet. No one else was there. Just me. I remember Sister Margherita holding out her arm, a wing of rustling black fabric directing me toward the array of food. She pointed to a simple, plastic tray bearing a plate, a glass, and silverware wrapped in a napkin. But it was the word on the paper napkin ring that undid me—one word meticulously rendered in crisp calligraphy: Elizabeth. I was dumbfounded. They cared enough to write my name on a napkin ring? And at once, the love described in childhood Bible lessons flooded in: "For I was hungry and you gave me food. I was thirsty and you gave me drink . . ." Because I was wounded and deeply weary, being the recipient of such no-strings-attached, unexpected love struck deep. After dinner, I returned to my room and sobbed for a good long while. I think the whole setup really tickled God.

The abbey's list of daily worship services read like this:

4:50 a.m. Vigils (apx. 1 hour)

6:45 a.m. Lauds (apx. 30 minutes)

After Mass: Terce (apx. 15 minutes)

11:45 a.m. Sext or Sext and None combined (apx. 15 minutes)

5: 00 p.m. Vespers (apx. 45 minutes)

7:30 p.m. Compline (apx. 30 minutes):

Compline is sometimes sung at 7:00 p.m. Please call ahead to check.

At my first early morning service, I arrived in the chapel before the nuns. The sisters soon appeared and took their seats in pews facing each other behind the altar. When they began to sing, I fumbled through the hymnbook and tried to keep up with the songs—Gregorian chants sung in Latin. As the ethereal sounds swung from one side of the altar to the other, back and forth, back and forth, I was transported into another realm. I wanted more. In fact, I was so dedicated to my spiritual mission that for the first few days, I attended all five services. Finally, Sister Margherita stopped me in the hall, softly touched my shoulder, and said, "Elizabeth, you don't have to attend *all* of the services."

I smiled, half disappointed, half relieved.

At one point during my retreat, I took a walk to a nearby field where I lay on the grass to watch the sky. After contemplating the clouds, I noticed a three-strand barbed wire fence that separated me from a black bull lying in the center of an adjoining field. As I watched the massive creature, I was possessed with the notion of testing my spiritual growth. If I crawled under the barbed wire, would he let me touch him? Had I evolved enough to pull this off? Apparently not, because I had trespassed only ten feet into his territory when he stood up, initiating my swift exit back under the fence. In all fairness, he might have been raised by hand and expected an ear of corn, but I chose the coward's course and fled.

All of this is to say I have gone to great lengths to learn and heal—to push my growth, observe my behavior, and learn how to fade headaches away.

Here is part of what I confirmed about myself, my understanding of God, and love: God is everywhere—St. Peter's Cathedral, sweat lodges, death, spring, winter, snow, oceans, rocks, and trees. Sparrows. Hawks. Mice. Busy streets. Mosquitos. God can be found in fear and anger. Everywhere I look, I find the same God, and help is always available for the very reasonable price of asking. I find that to be a very good deal.

My questions and answers change as I grow, and there's always room for improvement. That said, when I consider the intricacy of our galaxy, I'm not sure why it took me so long to relax about my life. I suspect it's due to the time it took for humility to outweigh my headache-producing ego, and even though I'm free of all but occasional, avoidable, slight headaches, I still work at letting go.

When I pray, cry out, call, ask, and seek, I find. I'm answered from within and without, and every time I hush my mind, my awareness opens to Infinite Wisdom.

James Dean was considered to be one of the world's greatest actors. He was imbued with the ability to take on a state of *being* the characters he portrayed. Numerous actors and acting coaches attempted to disassemble the art and craft of James Dean, and in dismembering the details, they killed their hopes of achieving similar greatness because separated parts do not equal a whole. That "special something," that unexplainable soul factor, is not something we can pick up with our hands. We cannot grab reflections in a mirror. We can only carry them within ourselves.

I have learned that God and I are connected at the heart, mind, and body. God does a lot of talking through both obvious and subtle messages transmitted through the responses of my body—awake or asleep. We work as a team—all the time.

I confess to knowing little, but I do know we contain the power mentioned by the great teacher, Jesus: "Greater things than these shall you do." I believe we are loaded with God-given ability, and I suspect at least a part of you believes it, too, irrespective of your connection to the Divine. If we keep going, asking, and communing, we can inhabit that "something greater" element of our being.

There is reason to trust in life and the ability of people to find their way through the quagmire of worldly yip-yap to the world of happiness and health. If I can do it, so can you. If I get a headache now, it's a little bitty thing compared to the monsters that used to run my life—and I know what caused it and how to fix it. (*Stop eating cheese. Stretch after biking.*)

If nothing else, I am evidence that miracles happen and that it's possible to unravel even the most tangled ball of human yarn in order to see the core of our simple beauty. It's there. I know this because I see it in everything, and I'm no different from anyone else. We, and all creatures in the universe, are part of God, and our journeys inevitably lead us to conclude that we are the ones we have been hoping to find. Loving ourselves inevitably increases our ability to love others and take action to save ourselves from suffering.

As Don Juan DeMarco said in the movie of the same name:

"There are only four questions of value in life:
What is Sacred?
Of what is the Spirit made?
What is worth living for?
What is worth dying for?
The answer to each is the same: only Love."
And love is a potent escape route from headaches.

#42

IN CONCLUSION
THE SIMPLE TRUTH

Champions keep playing until they get it right.

Billie Jean King

You are the only one who can find the solutions to your headaches because you are the only one who knows the details and dynamics of your particular life. All you need is the inspiration to act on your own behalf. If you have headaches, you are very likely intelligent, sensitive, and rich in spirit—and smart enough to have insight regarding your weak spots. Overwork? Ego? Defiance? Fear? At subconscious levels, you already know what needs adjusting, but you have to get out your personal toolbox and fix the machine—*you*. And, as you rummage through your tools, remember you can progressively add new ones.

One reason I follow the lessons I learned about headache release is because I was compelled to write a book—this one. When I started writing, I had already solved my monster headache problem but was so used to living with major pain that a bit of tension or a small headache was no big deal. So I cheated. I exercised and didn't stretch. I wouldn't eat a *whole* bag of potato chips, but I'd eat *half* a bag. I had a lackluster meditation practice, going weeks without walking in nature. I drank coffee. However, I found that there was no way to write a book about headaches without unflinching adherence to the methods I proclaimed. I *had* to clean up my act.

The final improvements to my regimen involved the elimination of caffeine and adverse foods and setting aside time to simply *be*. That's when the generalized tension in my body resolved itself and the small headaches vanished. I was delighted. Joy bounded into my life. I became invigorated, physically strong, and clear-minded. *Wow*.

If you are not motivated enough to make changes to your life, you may whip up some inspiration by making a list of the potential benefits of feeling energized and free of pain. Once you find your reasons, never let them go. Post your list where you can see it and read it whenever you're tempted to re-engage a bad habit. Put reminders around your home. You might put a beautiful antique key on your dresser (or in your pocket) to remind you that you possess the keys to free yourself from suffering. Let your prison door swing open and smell the fresh air of health and vigor. If you are not using your keys, you may want to ask yourself why. And, like me, you will want to keep an eye on your behavior, because in spite of what you know about headache triggers, it's possible to occasionally go kamikaze on yourself.

Case in point . . .

A few days ago, I awakened to a low-pressure weather system but drank two cups of coffee (decaf) anyway. Instead of eating a healthy lunch in the garden, I binged on cookies and a diluted cola in front of the television. My afternoon snack was salted popcorn, followed by chocolate. Throughout it all, I observed my self-sabotage (testing perhaps?). Naturally, my whacko behavior culminated in a *mother* of a headache that pounded all night and into the next day. Chastened, I knew enough to root around in my psycho-emotional basement for answers. When answers were not forthcoming, I called a temporary cease-fire and simply got back on track.

By now, you are familiar with the practices that reduce headache triggers, lift your threshold, and support freedom from headaches::

- Emotional truth-telling, release, and resolution.
- Bodywork (massage, acupuncture, chiropractic, Reiki).
- Healthful eating.
- The elimination of rebound drugs.
- Spiritual work.
- The elimination of the causes of bracing or tension.
- Finding new interests that make your heart sing.
- Hydration.
- Sleep.
- The creation of beautiful living spaces.
- Giving.
- Movement.
- Laughter.
- Stillness and rest.
- Communing with God.
- Time in nature.
- Deep breathing.
- Letting go.

Out of the countless physicians I saw through the years, not one of them put all of the components of Elizabeth Phelps (me) together to create a holistic view, much less create a plan for healing. Most of them had a fixed knowledge base with narrow parameters; they were not trained to view the human being as a whole, nor did they have the time to scrutinize my life. What physician has time to study the details of a person's unique thinking patterns, food habits, sleep habits, body type—all the things we've discussed in the pages of this book?

And what of emotional resolution—who's going to solve those issues for us? A doctor? A doctor cannot possibly know everything about the complex and miraculous creature that comprises you as a one-of-a-kind being. It took thirty years for someone to find an out-of-place piece of bone that caused my back to curve. I, alone, knew the depth of the teenage trauma, my particular emotional hurts, the snowboard wreck, the broken noses, my mental configuration. It would have taken anyone else a lifetime to consider the countless interrelated elements that affected my headaches. That's why I was the only one who could organize my puzzle pieces and link them together to form the healthy picture that is my life.

There are two voices. One whispers the truth. The other bangs out all manner of distraction. Choose the whispering voice, for it is the dependable voice, the all-knowing voice swirling within and around you.

The truth is, you *can* solve your headache dilemma. The answers reside within you, as does the capacity to find them.

Breathe.

You can do this.

EXTRAS

THE SESSION IN
THE DOCTOR'S OFFICE

In the introduction to *Unlocking the Headache Mystery*, I promised to share the process I used to pull an active headache from a patient I met while working in a physician's office. The patient's name was Mary. I disclose this experience to demonstrate the power of natural healing when the healer and the heal-ee work in communion with each other and the Divine. But before we get into Mary's session, let's talk about healing sessions in general.

A healing encounter is a complex two-way communication between a dedicated healer and an individual who sincerely wants to let go of an affliction. The healer is directed by information that comes from silent interactions between the parties. "Pulling headaches out" refers to mentally, physically, psychically, and energetically rekindling a person's innate ability to restore a state of harmony that, for our purposes, eliminates a headache.

Throughout a session, every word, thought, intention, and touch becomes a silent reminder to the individual: *It's okay. You are safe. You already know how to let go. It's okay to let go. It's okay to heal.* The sincerity of these sentiments must be absolute because most headache sufferers are encased in distrust and fear, and are long-removed from the natural state of ease that accompanies good health. That's why the healer must be 100% present, positive, and tuned in to the person in his or her care.

Healing sessions are hard to describe because they are organic—nuanced. They occur in a state of flux that reorganizes as the session proceeds. Even though you would have to be Mary to fully appreciate her session, I hope this demonstration encourages you to use the methods we've discussed throughout this book to ease your own headaches.

Again, if I can do it, you can do it.

THE SESSION

After Mary arrived, she met with Dr. Flip Flop (from the *Introduction*) and agreed to a healing session with me. We were introduced, of course, and then I escorted her into a quiet exam room. The room's view of rolling hills and blue sky provided the perfect atmosphere for healing, so I seated Mary facing the beautiful landscape (making sure the light didn't hurt her eyes). After she was comfortably situated, I shared my background and credentials, and then I gently asked her this question: "So, what do you think is the cause of your headaches?"

Mary shot the palm of one hand toward me in the STOP sign position and practically shouted, "I DO *NOT* WANT TO TALK ABOUT MY *MOTHER!* I HAVE HAD THESE HEADACHES SINCE I WAS A CHILD. I'M NOT GOING TO TALK ABOUT MY *MOTHER!* I DO *NOT* WANT TO TALK ABOUT MY *MOTHER!*"

Well, *Bingo!* the originating source of Mary's headaches was in the room with us—a real tiger, too. To help her feel safe, I reassured her by telling her the truth, "You don't have to do anything you don't want to do. You're completely in charge. It's okay. You don't *have* to discuss or *do* anything."

With the pressure removed and her authority restored, Mary's face and shoulders relaxed. Her breathing deepened.

We were on our way. Because deep breathing is vital to healing, I taught her how to breathe naturally, from the diaphragm like a baby or a puppy. (I refer to relaxed breathing as "puppy tummy breathing" because the image immediately suggests ease, innocence, and health.)

After Mary's breathing evened-out, I asked another permission (asking puts control where it belongs—with the individual). I told her, "I won't do anything to move your body, but I'd like to be able to gently touch certain meridians— especially your head, neck, shoulders, and back. Is that okay?"

"Sure."

"Do you like essential oils? Will a fragrance bother you?" Mary wasn't sure, so I didn't use oils during her session.

Because healing must begin with an attitude of openness to letting go, a measure of trust must be given to one's deeper self, the healer, and a higher source. So, to initiate our communion, I asked Mary if it was okay to start our session with a prayer. Mary welcomed the idea, so we called on Holy Beings to guide us. Our invocation identified her nature as sacred and ignited the flow of Reiki energy in my hands. Then I asked her to gently close her eyes, then guided her through a relaxation process that included the eyelashes, tongue, and bottoms of the feet, installing an unfamiliar pattern we would repeat throughout our time together.

During the session, information about Mary and the energy surrounding her body continuously flowed to me. My intuition led me to specific touchpoints. I applied light pressure to tight muscles, cleaned up and balanced her physical and etheric energies, and whispered words to encourage her to open the healing gateway in her mind. (I realize that description might sound gauzy to skeptics. Others familiar to mind-body practices will find them commonplace.) As I worked with Mary, I coordinated touch and words with the rhythm of her breath to release the tension evident in the bracing of her body—especially her neck, shoulders, back, and scalp.

With my hands gently resting on her shoulders, I told Mary, "You could let go of this tension and do everything you need to do in a peaceful state. It isn't helping you. *You are safe. You can let go now.*"

As I connected with Mary, I tuned into my inner world for direction and continuously empowered her with clearing techniques, supportive language, and therapeutic, distracting actions. Distraction momentarily confuses the mind and body and guides attention away from the headache. For instance, when I touched meridians on Mary's arm, I surprised her by simultaneously applying pressure to a foot and asking her to relax her tongue.

To relax the muscles at the top of her shoulders, I synchronized Mary's breathing (her in-breath) with light pressure on the top of one shoulder (the trapezius muscle), then released the pressure on her out-breath. This off-on "switch" allowed her to identify the difference between tension and relaxation. At the end of the third breath of the series, I flicked the tension out of her shoulders, and trailed my fingers down her arm so she could trace its path to her fingertips and out of her body. (It works.) After completing the process on both shoulders, I attended to her hands and fingers.

Here, I will emphasize that these physical actions are only effective when one's mind is "talking" to the tension in the individual's mind and body. This kind of pain-removal "surgery" only works when the practitioner's mind is so tuned-in to the individual that it temporarily becomes a part of them.

As I circled Mary, I touched points on her lower back, legs, and feet. I addressed the tension in her neck and worked my way to her scalp where I rolled my knuckles across strategic points on her head. I used my fingers and mind to move the headache toward the centerline on the top of her skull, then gathered it into a ball and mentally and physically pulled it out of her head. I repeated the process on the back of Mary's skull, then moved to touchpoints on her ears and face.

Reiki energy was at work throughout Mary's session. I reminded her to let her muscles "be like melted butter," an image I use repeatedly because it conjures relaxation and comfort.

When our session ended, I silently thanked the healing forces that helped us. When Mary opened her eyes, I gently moved my hand downward to provide a visual cue and said, "Now, stay low," to remind her to remain relaxed. Then I stepped out of the room to get her a glass of water and to give her a moment to experience her peaceful condition without my presence.

When I returned, I gave Mary the water, and then we quietly sat in the room—no rushing.

"How do you feel?"

"It's gone," she said.

"Completely?"

She nodded. "Yes."

I smiled, elated, and thanked Mary for her trust. I said, "Now, you've got it, keep it. Stay low. Let your muscles stay loose. Remember, melted butter muscles and puppy tummy breathing." After escorting her to the doctor's office, I wandered back down the hall to my desk. As I said in the introduction, Dr. Flip Flop and her colleagues were excited by the outcome of Mary's session and wanted me to help other patients, but the idea was halted due to legalities involving medical insurance. This is one reason such healing experiences are still rare in the world of Western medicine.

While treatments like Mary's are powerful and prove it's possible to eliminate an active headache, the results are temporary. Yes, Mary released her headache, but after reading this book, you know that to move toward permanent headache release, she would need to become an archeologist to her psyche and body and to examine root causes of her pain. She would have to create new behaviors to replace her long-standing headache habits. Nonetheless, our session was crucial. It was crucial because she realized she could achieve a headache-free, peaceful state naturally. She had remembered, for a while, who she really is—a safe, calm, powerful soul in a human body.

The most important take-away from this session is that incredible capabilities live within everyone, and we don't have to depend on the determinations of others to access them. If you can let go of a headache for an hour, you can let go of a headache for a day, a week—a year. Your success will take time and perseverance, but if you are dedicated to your health—your life—you can tune in to yourself and find your way to the peace-filled sunny side of the street.

RELAXATION EXERCISE:
THE MELTED BUTTER PUPPY-TUMMY
MIND-BODY SWEEP

My mother was ahead of her time and knew how to use her mind to relax her body. She taught me how to do it when I was a child. The practice came in handy when an ER doctor was rummaging around in my arm with a needle, trying to find a lost thorn—also useful when an ENT was lancing my eardrum. Fun things like that. Thanks to my mom, I was able to relax and reduce the pain. Through years of stitches and broken noses, I was able to modify my mother's relaxation methods to match the forms of pain that confronted me.

The original body scan technique requires focus, and the method is very specific. The exercise below includes a couple of twists I added to the fundamental scan. Here's how you can do it:

- Find a quiet location where you won't be interrupted.
- Place a glass of pure, filtered water within easy reach.
- Put a drop of your favorite essential oil on the inside of your left wrist, then circle your right wrist clockwise over it three times. Raise your wrists to your nose and take three deep breaths of the fragrance.
- Lie or sit comfortably.
- Take three more slow breaths. Take your time, and calmly breathe into the abdomen, letting the diaphragm extend outward. Use your mind to create a sense of peace. Sink into the stillness. Let gravity have you; feel your body weight pressing into the bed or chair.
- Move your attention to the very bottoms of your feet

and think, *My feet are relaxing* . . . Let your focus go to each toe, the top, sides, heels, arches, muscles, and tendons. Continue to breathe slowly. Let go of even the tiniest bit of tension in your feet.

⊚ Slowly slide your attention upward to your ankles. When you sense the slightest bracing, picture the tension leaving the feet and ankles with the exhale.

⊚ Mentally observe the tension floating out and up to the sky on the exhale; see it being purified into white light. On each inhale, breathe peace and calming blue light into your lungs.

⊚ Shift your focus slowly upward toward your calves. Picture them relaxing and think, *My calves are relaxing. I am feeling so relaxed lying down . . . I am relaxing more and more.* Continue to let go and slowly move upward through the knees, thighs, pelvis (aware of the front, back, and interior organs of your body), then ease through the mid-section, the lungs, and into your chest and shoulders. Go deep inside and take your time visiting each area. Relax your fingers, hands, wrists, forearms, and biceps. Feel the release of tension in your body—neck, throat, jaws, teeth, tongue, eyelashes, scalp muscles, forehead.

⊚ Breathe slowly. Keep saying lovely things to yourself as you let go. *My eyelids and brows, my eyelashes, my ears, are soooo relaxed, my scalp, my skull, my brain are so peaceful.* Let your muscles relax as if they are melting like warm butter.

When you have finished scanning your body, complete the exercise in the following way:

Revisit and relax the bottoms of your feet.
Breathe like a puppy from the tummy.
Revisit and relax your eyelashes.
Think "melted butter muscles."
Revisit and relax your tongue and your jaw.
Relax the bottoms of your feet again.
Relax your eyelashes again.
Sit or lie still.
Take another breath of the essential oil you previously put on your wrists.
Slowly wiggle your toes and fingers, and when you are fully awake, drink your water.

"Stay low" after you finish your relaxation practice. Go into the rest of your day or evening with a spirit of calm relaxation. Avoid chaos. If you sense tension at any time, remember the words, "melted butter muscles," relax your eyelashes and your tongue, and return to a sense of peace.

The more you practice, the easier it is to induce a sense of relaxed, headache-free living. Eventually, you can drop your tension level with one word.

SUGGESTED READINGS & MATERIALS

*You can find additional helpful wellness information at
TheHeadacheMystery.com.*

MIND, BODY & INNER LIFE

*Heal Your Headache: The 1-2-3 Program for Taking Charge of
Your Pain* by Dr. David Buchholz, MD *(2002)*
Why We Get Sick by Gabor Mate, MD (video, 2021)
Blink: The Power of Thinking Without Thinking by
Malcom Gladwell (2005)
Full Catastrophe Living by Jon Kabat-Zinn, PhD (2005)
You Can Heal Your Life by Louise Hay (1985)
Anatomy of an Illness by Norman Cousins (1979)
Ageless Body, Timeless Mind by Deepak Chopra, MD (1993)
The Dance of Anger by Harriet Lerner, PhD (1985)
Wheels of Life by Anodea Judith, PhD (1987)
Light on Yoga by B. K. S. Iyengar (1966)
The Apocrypha and selections from The Bible
The 7 Day Mental Diet by Emmet Fox (1935)
*Digital Nation, Season 28, Episode 9, Multi-Tasking in
America* – pbs.org/wgbh/pages/frontline/digitalnation
(2004)
The Law of Attraction by Esther and Jerry Hicks (2006)
I'm OK–You're OK by Thomas A. Harris, MD (1969)
*Spark Joy: An Illustrated Master Class on the Art of Organizing
and Tidying Up* by Marie Kondo (2016)
Feng Shui, The Book of Cures by Nancilee Wydra (1996)
Feng Shui for You and Your Cat by Alison Daniels (2000)
The Secret Lives of Color by Kassia St. Clair (2016)

The Power of Now by Eckhart Tolle (1999)

Callings by Gregg Lavoy (2017)

A Course in Miracles by Helen Schucman, Bill Thetford & Kenneth Wapnick – Foundation for Inner Peace (originally Columbia University) (1976)

Always We Begin Again, The Benedictine Way of Living by John McQuiston II (1996)

A New Earth by Eckhart Tolle (2005)

A Path with Heart, A Guide Through the Perils and Promises of Spiritual Life by Jack Kornfield (1993)

The Four Agreements: A Practical Guide to Personal Freedom by Don Miguel Ruiz (1997)

Way of the Peaceful Warrior by Dan Millman (1980)

The Actor by Don Miguel Ruiz with Barbara Emrys (2020)

Already Free by Bruce Tift (2015)

The Complete Works of Florence Scovel Shinn: The Game of Life and How to Play It; Your Word Is Your Wand; The Secret Door to Success; and The Power of the Spoken Word by Florence Scovel Shinn (1989)

Stretch, Unlock the Power of Less and Achieve More than you Ever Imagined by Scott Sonenshein (2017)

"Mastering the Art of Manifesting" by Wayne Dyer at Wanderlust's Speakeasy (video, 2013)

Alice in Wonderland directed by Tim Burton (film, 2010) based on *Through the Looking Glass* by Lewis Carroll

Mind Bell – App for smart phones

HEALING PROTOCOLS

Helping Yourself With Foot Reflexology by
Mildred Carter (1969)
The Relaxation Response by Herbert Benson, MD (1975)
Reference Guide for Essential Oils by Connie and
Alan Higley (1998)
Qigong Seated Mind-Body Practice by Dr. Roger Jahnke
(video) https://www.youtube.com/
watch?v=KTopFr1QM6g
Tune Up Therapy Equipment / TheHeadacheMystery.com
(credits to Jill Miller's Tune Up Fitness Worldwide,
tuneupfitness.com)
The Dizzy Cook cookbook and https://www.thedizzycook.com
by Alicia Wolf

ACKNOWLEDGEMENTS

My gratitude extends first to the Great Mystery that has surrounded my life and filled it with beauty, including the many gifted people who have attended the birth of this book.

For artistic, editorial, and writing support:

Everlasting thanks to Morgan Joseph Hamilton for creating the perfect cover art, and the brilliant touches he sprinkled throughout the book, even as he worked on his PhD. Most importantly, I am grateful that he is my Godson. I am deeply grateful to Adisti Slone for her input on the cover design, Deborah Morgenthal for putting her pro polish on the final manuscript, and Julia Stroud for her initial content consultation. Thanks to English-pro friend, Patty Northup (you didn't want to edit, but you did), and to kind relations and friends who scrutinized many, many, drafts and repeatedly picked me up when writing the book left me lying like a puddle on the floor: Janet McDonald, Florence Patrice Lively, Carol Anne Brown, Deborah Shook, Bob Nemens, Cheri Nemens, Bobby and Sarah Brownlee, Bob Maldonado, Jennifer Glover, Elise Gordon, Cheri Collins, Denny Mason, Michael Wheeler, Frye Gaillard, and Vandorn Hinnant. I thank my clever friend, John Woods, for smoothing countless bumps along the publication highway, and benevolent Jennifer Glover for the hours she spent sharing her love and expertise. Special thanks to Marcy Anderson for my years in The Fairhope Writer's Forum, and to Nolan White for his cheerleading. Big thanks to my Leopard Forest friends who repeatedly provided creative reviews.

To my wellness guides:

Everlasting thanks to the holistic practitioners and healers who delivered me from pain and taught me how to heal myself. Blessings to the doctors and therapists who, in their own way, helped me, including the staff at the Diamond Headache Clinic, the Cleveland Clinic, and The Friary on the Shore—Dr. Susan Danahy, Joy, Mike, and others. Enormous thanks to Dr. David Buchholz for finanlizing my healing through his cutting edge headache solutions and book, and for sharing his time in conversing with me and offering notes on *Unlocking the Headache Mystery*. Big gratitude to Dr. Elise Gordon for her integrity, support, and lenghty conversations about healing. Thank you, most genuinely, to readers and fellow travelers doing the courageous work of healing their lives.

To my loving and generous tribe:

The list of beautiful family and friends who supported me through years of completing this book is long. You know I know you know I know who you are, and your names are embroidered on my heart: Heather, Deborah, Becky, Holly & John, Carol Anne, Hal & Barbara, Belmont, Don & Carol Lynn, Mita, Florence, Betsy, Lesley, De, Nancy, Morgan, Jennifer, Helen, Carol, Eileen, Patty & Steve, Ellen & Bob, John, Cherie & Bob, George, Randal, Kathleen, Tamlin, Shawn, Wendy, Sarah, Bruce, Lovelace, Frank, D.J., Ann, Claude & Anne, Craig, Sarah, Karen, Kathleen, William, Jamie & Terry, Mark, Ida, and Mike.

To longtime friend-sister, Deb Shook, I say, "Go, possums!" Brunie Emmanuel, thank you for being my Friend (capital "F") for life. Morgan Hamilton, you are the definition of Godsend. Holly and John Algee, you have my ongoing Holy, Holy, Holy Thanks. A round of applause for Jason Elledge who kept my computer running properly, even on Sundays. Big thanks to Luanne and John Matson for the sweet editing and rest retreats.

Vast thanks to my family and friends for gifts of time, energy, and love throughout the good news, bad news phases of my life. I will never be able to repay Louis F. Ray, Jr. for living through some of the worst headache years as my dedicated husband, and later as my friend. Heather Smith, thank God we are blood. Becky Orlich, you are an important stake in the ground of my life.

Deep love to my beloved cat, Balthezar, for traveling many miles and sacrificing playtime for the writing of *Unlocking the Headache Mystery*, and to Storybook, for the times she begged me to play when I had my face stuck in a computer screen.

ALPHABETICAL INDEX

Please add your review of *Unlocking the Headache Mystery, Essential Keys to Your Vibrant Life* on Amazon.com.

You can find information about coaching, presentations, and workshops at www.TheHeadacheMystery.com. The website also includes links to instructional information, Tune Up Fitness Worldwide Therapy Balls, and other helpful materials.

Thank you, and I hope you keep in touch. I would love to hear about your healing journey.
Contact me through TheHeadacheMystery.com

NOTES

NOTES

NOTES

NOTES

NOTES

NOTES

Made in the USA
Coppell, TX
28 August 2022

82189891R00164